DESIGNER'S
POSTPRESS
COMPANION

by Malcolm G. Keif

National Association for Printing Leadership
Paramus, New Jersey

Senior Staff Director, Communications: Dawn A. Lospaluto
Director, Publications: Richard S. Papale

Editor: Erika Kendra; *Editorial Assistant:* Andra Bell

Cover Design: Erika Kendra

ISBN 1-929734-43-3

CONTENTS

CONTENTS

CONTENTS

CONTENTS

CONTENTS

ACKNOWLEDGEMENTS

This book is dedicated to my wife, Laura, and my sons, Adam and Treacy. Thank you for your love and support throughout this project.

I gratefully acknowledge the technical advice, training, and support received from:

- Gregory L. Berry

- Rick Campbell, Wrap-Ups, Inc.

- Arthur Crawley, Kolbus, Inc.

- Jim DeCrevel, DeCrevel Embossing and Stamping Dies

- Red Heesch, Cal Poly State University

- Jonathon Niezing, Wrap-Ups, Inc.

- Bob Pinkin, Cal Poly State University

Special thanks to my father, Rodney G. Keif, for his tireless editing efforts; Erika Kendra for her excellent project management and illustration work; and Richard Papale, NAPL's publisher, for making this book possible.

I thank my colleagues and students at Cal Poly State University, where I am daily challenged. You continually stimulate me to grow and pursue excellence in everything I do. For my colleagues at Central Missouri State University, I thank you for the many great years we worked side-by-side in educating graphic communication students for employment. May design, printing, and postpress be thriving industries for centuries to come.

INTRODUCTION

Postpress has long been an afterthought of the printing processes, but in reality is the most important step in the production of printing. It is the facet of production where a job that was handled perfectly in design, prepress, and press could be ruined. It is where the smallest of errors can result in the highest cost of correcting errors — redesigning or reprinting the entire job. Hence, postpress is the printing production cost center requiring enormous accuracy and attention to details. In fact, the attention to postpress begins in the design phase of printing.

Postpress is where the incorrect placement of images on a page, being off 1/32 of an inch in a trim, having one wrongly collated signature, or a misplaced stitch, can mean the difference between success or failure of a printing job. It can mean the difference between printing being produced profitably or produced at a loss.

It is for these reasons that *Designer's Postpress Companion*, by Dr. Malcolm Keif, is a vital resource for designers and anyone else planning and producing printing.

No other publication on the subject covers the topics of postpress as comprehensively as the *Designer's Postpress Companion*. Dr. Keif's treatment of what the designer should know about postpress is unparalleled by anything previously written on the subject. Topics covering the printing production environment through issues related to mailing and distribution are vital in relating design to the various intermediate postpress processes such as cutting, die-cutting, folding, stitching, foil stamping, embossing, packaging, and more.

While written particularly for designers, the *Designer's Postpress Companion* provides important insights for people involved in all aspects of print planning and production on how to successfully complete the finishing processes. Dr. Keif's book clearly explains the relationship between postpress and design as well as it does the relationships between prepress, press, and postpress. The *Designer's Postpress Companion* is also an excellent reference book for schools that teach graphic arts and for professional education within the design and printing industries.

Harvey Robert Levenson, Ph. D.
Department Head, Graphic Communication Department
California Polytechnic State University, San Luis Obispo

CHAPTER 1

A CASE FOR POSTPRESS

The ambition of marketing professionals — including designers — is to influence a buying decision. Advertising is built on the premise that the right message, in the right package, can persuade individuals to purchase *your* particular product.

But just what is the right package to deliver your message?

Postpress answers this question.

Print communication is multi-sensory, engaging the eyes, incorporating touch, sound, and even smell. Print can be simultaneously subtle and vibrant. The soft background of a cream text stock contrasted against an energetic mirror-like gold foil stamp is an amazing tool to attract attention.

Multiple senses are engaged with print. Who doesn't relate to the elegant sensation of an embossed greeting card? Or consider the different textures associated with a book containing glossy paper contrasted with a felt-finished text stock. Listen to the crisp sound that paper projects as you leaf through a new coffee-table book. Even the *swishing* of your newspaper is memorable. Can you still smell the ink in a recently delivered magazine or catalog?

Print is familiar, personal, and trusted. It can send a message of value elegance, richness, and enthusiasm. Effective print can rival any marketing campaign on response rate. Print is used for countless applications, including enticing a buying decision or sealing a contract.

The *right package* incorporates the best *form*, *decoration*, and *distribution* to convey your message. Postpress gives physical form to your message. It puts the finishing touches on design. Postpress also provides the optimum distribution strategy. Your choices for postpress operations will make the difference between a book, folder, flyer, or carton that sells — and one that sits.

Postpress enhances the sophisticated craftsmanship of the lithographer by giving shape to the product. It adds function and adornment and delivers the product in a usable, convenient form. Without postpress, there would be no book, no relief, and no dimension.

WHAT IS POSTPRESS?

Ink is applied to flat sheets. Then what? As its name implies, postpress encompasses those print production steps that occur after the printing press. Postpress operations typically fall into three broad categories:

- **Binding** functions, including cutting, folding, and book binding (in other words, the form)

- **Finishing** operations, including foil stamping, embossing, and die cutting (decoration)

- **Distribution** strategies, including packaging, shipping, and delivery (distribution)

The most basic postpress process, cutting, is central to the printing operation and is utilized for nearly every job. Because printed pieces are frequently produced two or more at a time, cutting is needed to separate those pieces.

There are other common postpress or bindery functions. For example, many flyers require folding. Hand folding is possible, but large-volume machine folding is much more efficient.

Bookbinding is another important process in postpress workflow. Whether you intend to wire stitch, adhesive bind, spiral bind, or use a hard cover, a book with an appropriate binding conveys quality and functionality.

Postpress also entails the decorative functions of embossing, foil stamping, or foil embossing. These high-value techniques help pieces stand out from their competition. Each process provides significant importance in certain markets.

Packaging, mailing, and delivery are other key components of a comprehensive postpress strategy. The effective designer considers all value propositions for a print job, including proper packaging. Product integrity, ease of transportation, verifying product counts, and ease of access are all important packaging components.

Professional warehousing, kitting, or fulfillment may add additional functionality for your client. Kitting multiple components into one cohesive package involves expertise. Managing data, inventory, and retrieval systems make fulfillment and kitting a valuable postpress component.

Without a comprehensive postpress plan, the designer relegates the final product to chance. The skilled designer considers all options, and selects those that provide the greatest value within budget. Without question, increasing your knowledge of postpress operations will increase the success of all your projects.

THE DESIGNER'S TOOLBOX

Every designer has a toolbox. It contains pencils, erasers, brushes, ink pens, and templates. Of course, today the tools may be digital and the toolbox virtual, but the outcome is a professional expression of yourself and your concept. Designer Saul Bass said it well, "Anything but boring." That is the worst crime — that is, of course, unless your design overshadows your message. As you make creative decisions, build an image that will enhance your message, not distract from it.

Your design toolbox should contain a variety of tools in each of the three postpress areas — binding, finishing, and distribution. Postpress strategies expand your design toolbox, provide additional solutions, and give your designs added power. As your skills improve, you will discover new tools and learn different techniques for applying existing tools.

Increased production knowledge ensures the smooth manufacturing of your projects. Understanding paper grain direction, for example, will significantly improve your brochures, books, or even a table tent for the local café. Although producing these details belongs to the printer, your knowledge base will be an invaluable resource. Experience leads to better work at lower costs.

Your projects may have greater impact by using less conventional decorating options, such as multiple varnishes and coatings, foil stamping, or embossing to draw the eye to the printed graphics. Other designers use extended gamut colors and spot colors to make an image "pop." Of course, white space can also be very effective.

Printing offers great stimulation for the eye; but tapping into other senses, such as touch, can be a powerful communication tool. Why not explore touch, sound, or smell as part of the overall user experience? Effective design often captures two or more sensorial expressions.

Designers have a wealth of postpress options at their disposal. If, for example, you are designing a book, you can choose spiral or comb binding, Wire-O®, posts, saddle-stitching, adhesive binding, or sewn case binding. Your choice depends on your (or your client's) goal for the final product. Is the book thick or thin? Is the book subjected to heavy use? Does the book need to lie flat? Is the book intended to be functional (such as a textbook) or is it primarily decorative (such as a special edition of a novel)?

Different postpress options can produce the same overall result — in this example, a bound book. However, each method has benefits that provide a unique user experience. Understanding the available options will enhance your ability to present your message both efficiently and effectively, and will significantly increase your value to your clients.

The effective designer plans every aspect of postpress, including distribution strategies that add greatest value to the project. Perceptive designers understand the U.S. Postal Service requirements, and produce direct mail that qualifies for substantial postal

> Do you regularly have problems with your printer? Can't find one that can "get the job done right"? If so, consider your role in the solution. As your skills and knowledge grow, you will provide better communication about the execution of postpress applications. Of course, always rely on professionals for their production expertise.

discounts. Shipping, shrink-wrapping, or banding options can provide benefits for product protection and quantity verification.

FORM

In addition to choosing paper and fonts, designers define the form of the finished product. A fundamental question for any designer is, "What shape will the final project take?"

For example, you decide the form of an advertising brochure. Will it deliver flat? Folded? What type of fold? Should it be a booklet? How many pages? Should it bind or simply be single sheets with three holes for insertion into a binder?

All of these questions are crucial to the structure of the document. How a project is folded or bound drastically impacts its usability. As you grow in understanding the advantages, disadvantages, and production limitations of each postpress operation, you will design your artwork within the limitations of the equipment.

When considering form, cost is certainly a major factor. However, each postpress operation offers unique benefits that may overcome price objections. For example, three-ring binding is one of the few methods in which the end user can modify the book content, which is important for frequently updated products such as catalogs. In books where removing or replacing pages is discouraged, three-ring binding provides a distinct *dis*advantage.

DECORATION

Some of the most creative design work is achieved with postpress decorating strategies, called finishing operations. These may be performed by the printer, but are often outsourced to specialized trade finishers.

Finishing techniques include hot foil stamping, blind embossing, foil embossing, die cutting, scoring, laminating, and even hand assembly of capacity folders or specialty pieces. While many of these operations impact utility and even form, most are decorative in nature and are used as design tools. Wine labels, collateral pieces, and greeting cards utilize foil stamping, embossing, and die cutting. Each example incorporates postpress finishing operations as key design elements, increasing decorative options for the designer and adding value for the client.

Consider a wine label. The bright, reflective foil catches the eye and conveys a sense of elegance or royalty. Perhaps more than any other food or beverage, wine relies heavily on the label for sales. It is estimated that at a given

Figure 1-1. Wine labels often use multiple finishing technques.

price point, ninety percent of wine purchases are based on the label design. Because of this influence, no expense is spared in the design and production of wine labels. They are decorated with hot foils, embossing, and die cut edges to influence point-of-sale decisions.

Hot foil stamping uses a shaped, heated die to transfer a thin, colored aluminum foil to a substrate. A variety of foil patterns and colors are available to meet different applications. The result is highly reflective type and graphics that contrast with the paper or print. The colored foil catches the eye by reflecting light and shimmering as the consumer walks past the bottle on the shelf.

Embossing is a method used to create three-dimensional effects with paper. Braille, used to aid the blind in reading, is a widely known example of embossing. Most embossing is purely decorative, providing a unique three-dimensional look and feel. Embossing deforms the paper without damaging it; actually, it *reforms* paper into the shape of the die.

Some papers distort better than others, allowing very deep embosses. In general, bulky uncoated stocks work best. Very thin stocks tend to rebound after the paper has been formed; they do not hold an emboss well and should be avoided. To achieve the best possible result, you should discuss paper selection with your postpress provider.

DISTRIBUTION

Distribution strategies include drop shipment, mailing, warehousing, and fulfillment, along with appropriate packaging and imaging to complete these operations.

Clients want high-quality work, faster and cheaper than ever before. Reducing cycle time is an increasingly critical factor in print procurement. Just-in-time, lean manufacturing strategies involve having product support pieces in place at the right moment — not too early, tying up precious resources, and not too late, forcing product delays.

Basic understanding, combined with good resources, prepares you to make informed, cost-efficient decisions. As an example, test your knowledge of U.S. postal requirements with the following questions:

- What are the four primary strategies for receiving postal discounts on large mailings?
- What are the guidelines for placement of a barcode?
- What do the numbers of the zip+4 mean?
- What is the correct aspect ratio for letters to be processed through USPS sorting machinery?

Knowing the answers to these questions — and designing your products accordingly — can result in significant cost savings. Perhaps more importantly, *not* knowing the answers to these questions can add substantial — and unnecessary — cost to your project budget. The good news is that the U.S. Postal Service commissions direct-mail design analysts to work directly with designers to produce well-prepared mailings. (Mailing strategies are discussed in Chapter 14.)

Distribution is as important to good design as selecting the best font. Technique does not end with learning how to select and edit a portion of a photograph. Skill and knowledge in distribution is critical for the success of all your printed projects. Otherwise, last-minute decisions will lead to limited — and possibly expensive — distribution choices.

If you serve as a consultant to your customers about every aspect of the business, you become an indispensable asset. Knowledge about the entire print supply chain gives you a competitive edge.

BEGIN WITH THE END IN MIND

As you begin any design work, consider the end user.

- Who is your audience?
- What are their interests?
- What experience do you want them to have?
- What motivates their buying decisions?

Your goal is to communicate a compelling message to persuade, inform, or entertain. Although you may have limited control over the message — how you package this message is vital.

As you focus on designing for postpress, you should ask three basic questions.

1. What form should the printed piece take?
2. Will any decorating techniques increase sales beyond investment?
3. What is the most advantageous way to distribute the product?

POSTPRESS PLANNING

Planning is the key to smooth production. The general strategy is to conceptualize forward, then plan backwards. After you have a general idea of the form and design for your piece, start backwards by planning distribution.

You need to consider the project budget in the early conceptual stages. If you have a very small budget, you should not plan to print eight colors with custom folds, die cuts, and foil embossing.

Consider this example of distribution planning: flyers are to be rubber-banded in groups of fifty, and then packed 2,500 per carton, placed on pallets, and stretched-wrap. The pallets will then be placed on a truck and shipped to the customer's dock.

A cheaper plan would be to skip cartons, stack the flyers directly on a pallet, and stretch-wrap the pallet. Using this alternative, however, it is likely that numerous pieces would be damaged in the distribution process. Packaging smaller lots typically provides greater protection for the product, but packaging impacts price. It is best to consider these expenses from the beginning.

After planning your distribution strategies, you should next consider binding options. How will a book be assembled? Some binding methods (such as perfect binding, spiral binding, and ring binding) require a large gutter area; some stack single sheets; others insert folded signatures one inside another.

Although press sheet layout is typically implemented by the printer, your understanding of layout could impact price. For example, putting common spot colors on pages that print on the same press sheet may reduce cost. You should discuss imposition with your printer in advance to determine if efficiencies can be gained by knowing where the pages are positioned on the press sheets.

Page dimensions are important when planning a design. For example, significant price breaks may be realized by conforming to standard paper sizes. Remember, press sheets may have other control images printed on them. Your printer can help you to determine the optimum press sheet size.

You also need to consider grain direction (discussed in Chapter 2) when planning for folds and books. Like press sheet layout, this is technically the printer's responsibility, but the right questions on your part might avoid costs and delays, and ensure crisp folds with no cracks.

When planning for foil stamping or embossing, you should consult with the finisher about compatibility of the foil or emboss on the stock you have chosen. As a rule, smoother papers will foil stamp better, and bulkier, softer papers will emboss better. Unless you have experience with a particular stock, consult the finisher prior to selecting the paper, stamp characteristics, or bevel for embossing.

You can see from these few examples that a knowledgeable designer significantly improves the outcome by thoroughly planning a job.

THE "COST" OF POSTPRESS

What is the *true* cost of postpress? The answer, of course, depends on the complexity of the job. Postpress cost is usually a small fraction of overall production costs — typically less than fifteen percent.

The cost of poor postpress, however, is devastating, requiring expensive and rushed reruns. It is essential that postpress be planned and executed correctly. While you have minimal control over the postpress execution, you have significant control in planning and preparing your files to minimize errors. The more you know about postpress, the better you will plan, communicate, and avoid mistakes. The more you know about postpress, the more persuasive your projects will be for your clients.

Print purchasing habits have changed. The old model was to buy a large quantity to reduce the *price per piece.* Today, print buyers focus on the *price per response* or sale. This is true in commercial printing and, to a lesser degree, in point-of-purchase packaging. When you purchase value-added or premium services such as die cutting or foil stamping, you expect results. If your design elicits a greater response, you can confidently justify higher per-piece costs.

RECOGNIZING YOUR RESOURCES

The most successful people surround themselves with knowledgeable people. Throughout this book, I will mention people who I believe should be able to assist you in planning postpress solutions. You can tap into the expertise of your printer, paper vendors, other designers, trade binders, and finishers. And don't forget the U.S. Postal Service; their Mailpiece Design Analysts are ready to help you in preparing print for efficient mailing.

CHAPTER 2

THE PRINT PRODUCTION ENVIRONMENT

Printing is a series of production steps, each building upon the other. The more coordinated these steps are, the better the final product will be. Each person or department must prepare materials that optimize production in subsequent steps. When viewed as a complete system, interrelationships are paramount.

A "SYSTEMS" APPROACH

Postpress, the last link in a chain of events, relies on well-designed, planned, and executed production. Time squandered in other operations forces postpress to make up time to deliver on schedule. The experienced designer recognizes this danger and works to provide files that are error-free, press- and postpress-friendly. Each component must provide the highest-quality materials for hand-off.

Press sheets must be delivered to postpress printed in a logical and agreed-upon way. They should be easily cut. All signatures (discussed in detail later in this chapter) should be identical in layout. They must be folded in the desired manner. Press sheets must have all the correct control marks on them. Every detail should be considered and executed so that postpress receives precision materials to which value is added.

As a designer, you are the first link in the production chain. Your responsibility is huge, as any error in the beginning has ramifications throughout the system. You are part of a system. Your digital files should be prepared in a manner that optimizes every step of production.

WHO ARE THE PLAYERS?

The major players in the print production cycle are the client; the designer; the prepress department; the press department; and the postpress department. In some cases, several of these roles are filled by the same person or provider — for example, many printing companies have prepress, press, and postpress departments, and some have designers on staff.

Other companies might outsource some or all of the production processes. Many printers will cut and fold, but send foil stamping and embossing to a trade finisher. In these situations, the printing company, rather than the designer or client, usually subcontracts the finishing.

Many supply chain variations exist. Sometimes print brokers are involved. Advertising agencies may be players. Knowing the components of the system, and who works for whom, is important.

In the postpress world, there are four types of companies:

- A commercial printer with in-house postpress operations

- A trade bindery, providing cutting, folding, and binding services to printing companies

- A trade finisher, providing foil stamping, embossing, and die cutting to printing companies

- Mailing houses, which specialize in preparing mail projects

In recent years, the lines have blurred. Many trade finishers now offer bindery or mailing services. Printers increasingly expand services to include binding, finishing, and mailing operations. Mailing houses now produce commercial printing.

You may want to tour some of the companies with whom you work. They likely take pride in their work and welcome a chance to show off their facilities. Most enjoy developing closer relationships with their customers and end-users.

THE DESIGNER'S RESPONSIBILITY

Is it your problem if your files create production difficulties? On one hand, creative designs drive new production techniques and standards. Printers are constantly challenged by the creative community to make production advancements. Modern presses offer much better print fidelity and consistency than presses a decade ago — largely due to designers' demands to lay down more ink and maintain color over a long run.

There is the other side of this coin. Wise designers understand the limitations of printing. They work to create designs that are effective and relatively simple to produce.

Printers possess drastically different skill levels. The best win national awards and pride themselves on producing vibrant reproductions; their books are clean with excellent crossovers; their products contain few defects. There are also printers that pride themselves on producing work at a minimal cost; they focus on using inexpensive, efficient processes. You should expect different end-results and pricing from these two types of printers.

Designers prepare artwork based on details about the product and benefits to the audience. The effective designer considers the expertise of those who will reproduce the artwork. If the budget allows only for the cheapest printing and postpress work available, complex designs should be avoided. If the budget is unlimited, you can confidently design complex postpress work that will be executed well.

It is possible to design work that no one can reproduce well. The question of blame is immaterial, because blame does not solve the problem. The best designers learn; they don't repeat mistakes. They don't deliver files that repeatedly require excessive corrections. Your value as a designer rests on your ability to generate clean files.

So, back to the previous question. It *is* your problem when your files create problems if you don't know the limitations of the processes. It is okay to challenge those limitations, but don't overcomplicate your work if it is not necessary. Simple designs that are easy to reproduce can be very effective. If you consistently provide clean, simple work, your suppliers will reward you with the best pricing.

PRODUCTION PLANNING

Production planning involves considering all necessary steps for efficient print production. What goes into a production plan? First, the planner identifies which operations are needed: preflighting, imposition, trapping, ripping, film and/or plate output, press, cutting, folding, stitching, shrink wrapping, carton packing, and shipping. After the general steps are identified, increased detail is scrutinized.

Production planning is worked backwards. Postpress is planned first, then press, and then finally prepress.

A well-printed sheet with accurate bindery marks facilitates smooth postpress production. The planner first determines the necessary folding, scoring, finishing, binding, packaging, and distribution steps.

During planning, the type and number of printing plates are identified. Ink colors and sequence are specified. Workflow, equipment, and all other production details are examined. The paper quantity is determined and all materials are ordered. Production planning recognizes the likelihood that some waste will occur at each production step, and arranges for excess materials accordingly.

After press has been considered, the planner specifies the appropriate prepress information, including correct trapping and workflow needs. The planner also identifies the optimal press sheet layout (imposition) based on available paper sizes.

A job ticket is generated and a production schedule, containing all the relevant job information, is set.

The job begins upon receipt of digital files from the designer.

PAPER KNOWLEDGE

Substrate selection is one way you can impact performance in postpress. It is very important to understand paper variables that influence quality. A *substrate* is the base material for printing, usually paper, paperboard, or plastic. Other less common substrates include foil, metallized paper, sheet metal, or wood. Most commercial designers work extensively with paper.

Paper is wood pulp that has been reformed into thin sheets. Cellulose fiber is separated from the tree bark and other proteins, bleached, and then sprayed out in a water solution onto a mesh wire. The water is then progressively removed. Papermaking machines (called *fourdriniers*) transport paper down the wire against an absorbent felt, and on into dryers. As the paper moves through the process, the water content is lowered to approximately five percent. If the paper is to be coated, it is taken off-line, where china clay or other pigments are added to the surface of the sheet, and then *calendared* or ironed to a smooth finish.

Grain Direction

The wire motion made on these machines during manufacturing gives the paper a characteristic called *grain direction*. You may have noticed that when you tear a coupon out of a newspaper, it tears straight in one direction and zig-zags back and forth in the other direction. Grain direction is the tendency of the cellulose fiber to align itself as the wire moves. Most of the fiber aligns in one direction, which influences characteristics like tear strength and ease of folding.

Visualize a straw mat. Now imagine rolling the mat up. The mat rolls easily in one direction — with the straw — but not well against the straw direction. Like the straw mat, paper folds and tears more easily in one direction than the other, particularly with heavier stocks. We describe a fold as either *with the grain* or *against the grain*. With the grain means that the fold is parallel to the grain of the paper. This provides the cleanest fold; it will be sharper and provide less cracking of the paper surface than a cross-grain fold.

In the case of the newspaper coupon, when it tears straight, you are tearing with the grain. When the tear zig-zags, you are tearing across the grain.

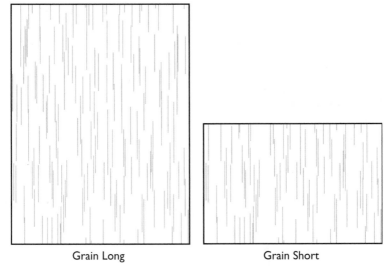

Grain Long   Grain Short

Figure 2-1. Paper grain direction is relative to the dimensions of the sheet.

Paper can be purchased either *grain long* or *grain short*, referring to the grain direction relative to the dimensions of the stock. Grain long means that the grain direction is running parallel to the long dimension of the sheet. If you cut the long dimension in half, you change the paper to grain short. Not all papers are available both grain short and grain long.

Grain direction is an important factor in printing. Grain direction influences the orientation a sheet may run on the press. Grain direction is even more critical in postpress, and always takes precedence over a press operator's desires. Generally, folds should be parallel to the paper grain. Of course, this is not always possible; many jobs use right-angle folds, requiring at least one fold perpendicular to the grain.

When producing books, the paper should be laid out so grain direction is parallel to the spine, for both the interior and the cover, resulting in a stronger book with straight sheets. Correct grain direction is more critical in perfect-bound and case-bound books than saddle-stitched books. You should never alternate grain direction in a book; all pages must be the same.

Paper Size

Since paper is made in large rolls, you might assume that paper can be purchased in any size. To a degree that is true. You may order direct from the paper mill if your quantity is large enough and sufficient lead-time is granted. But if you order less than a railroad-car load and lead-time is insufficient, you are limited to the sizes in your local paper merchant's inventory. This reality usually prevents perfect layouts. In most cases, pieces are run on oversized sheets with the waste discarded.

BASIS WEIGHT

There are several categories of paper: bond, book, cover, newsprint, and others. Each of these has a specific *basic size*, which is the size used to determine basis weight (see Table 1).

> Most papers are never actually cut to the basic size because basis weight can be interpolated at any size.

When cut to the basic size, the weight of one ream (five hundred sheets) is determined — called *basis weight*. If a ream of book paper cut to 25 × 38 in. weighs 70 lb., it is called 70-lb. book or substance 70 (sub 70). Typical basis weights of book papers are 50, 60, 70, 80, and 100 (although other weights are also available). Papers are available in various basis weights. The weight of paper impacts its thickness and stiffness; a higher basis weight indicates thicker paper.

Basis weights correlate only to others within a paper category. In other words, 60-lb. book paper is heavier than 50-lb. book paper. When you cross into different paper categories, basis weights cannot be easily compared. For example, 50-lb. book is actually lighter than 24-lb. bond.

Because the basic size of bond paper is smaller than that of book paper, it is logical that reams cut to this size would weigh less, even if they are in fact thicker, heavier papers. Typical bond weights are 20-, 24-, and 28-lb. Are they lighter than book papers? Not always.

The geometric area of basic-size bond paper (17 × 22 in., or 374 sq. in.) is approximately 40% of the area of basic-size book paper (25 × 38 in., or 950 sq. in.) This means that an equivalent weight bond paper would be 40% of the book paper basis weight. For example, sub 24 bond is roughly equivalent in weight to a sub 60 book (60 × 0.40 = 24).

Cover papers use yet a different basic size. Smaller than the basis size for book stock, it is logical that the basis weights are lower, because we are weighing five hundred sheets of a smaller size. Common cover basis weights are sub 65, 80, and 100. Cover stocks are much thicker, heavier papers than book paper, since they weigh equivalent amounts in smaller dimensions. The bottom line is that you can only easily compare basis weights within a category (unless you do the math).

> **Bond vs. Book Stock**
>
> Can you substitute 24-lb. bond for 60-lb. book? Yes. However, the sheet opacity is lower in bond paper. Bond papers are made with the intention of printing on one side only and don't have the opacifying additives of book papers.

Paper Category	Basic Size	Basis Weights
Bond (Business papers)	17 × 22 in.	16, 20, 24, 28
Book Papers	25 × 38 in.	40, 45, 50, 55, 60, 70, 80, 100
Cover Papers	20 × 26 in.	60, 65, 80, 100
Newsprint	24 × 36 in.	28, 30, 32
Index	25.5 × 30.5 in.	90, 110

Table A. The basic size and basis weight of commonly used papers.

COATINGS

Coated papers are very popular for their ability to hold ink on the surface, resulting in good color fidelity. Coated papers are made in gloss, dull, and matte finishes. The difference is the degree of specular reflectance or shininess. Gloss-coated sheets are shiny — important for attracting attention. However, gloss papers make reading large amounts of text difficult.

Coated papers can introduce postpress problems. For example, perfect binding of coated stocks can be difficult, since glue will not penetrate these papers as well as uncoated stocks. Further, dull and matte stocks are susceptible to marking or scuffing during postpress operations. Generally, uncoated sheets don't have as many postpress problems as coated sheets.

GRADING

Most papers receive a quality grade. For white papers, the grade is largely determined by the brightness of the sheet. *Brightness* is defined as the reflectance of blue light. Therefore, sheets that reflect a large amount of blue light are considered bright and receive a grade of 1. Sheets that are rather gray and don't reflect blue light are called number 5 sheets. Different types of papers use different grading scales. Super Calendared (SC) papers, used in retail inserts and catalogs, grade on gloss.

Generally, number 5 sheets contain a protein called *lignen*, resulting in yellowing and deterioration with age. This protein can be removed during the pulping stage to produce higher-grade papers. When you leave newsprint out in the sun, it is easy to see the effects of lignen.

> Why isn't lignen always removed? Simply put, it is cheaper to leave it in and pass the savings on to the customer.

Grade Group	Grade	Description	Type	TAPPI/ISO Brightness	% Gloss
Coated	Premium No. I	Coated Free-Sheet	Coated	≥ 88.0	
	No. I	Coated Free-Sheet	Coated	85.0 - 87.9	
	No. 2	Coated Free-Sheet	Coated	83.0 - 84.9	
	No. 3	Coated Free-Sheet	Coated	79.0 - 82.9	
	No. 4	Coated Free-Sheet or Coated Groundwood	Coated	73.0 - 78.9	
	No. 5	Coated Groundwood	Coated	< 72.9	
Uncoated Groundwood	SC-A+	SC	Uncoated		50
	SC-A	SC	Uncoated		45
	SC-B+	SC	Uncoated		40
	SC-B	SC	Uncoated		30

Table B. Paper substrate grade classifications.

RECYCLED PAPERS

Recycled papers are popular for their benefits to the environment. They are made by recovering fiber from waste paper. Recycled fiber is not as long or strong as new fiber, so some recycled papers mix recovered fiber with virgin fiber for increased strength and smoothness. The surface of recycled stock can also be very abrasive.

Recycled stocks can cause problems in postpress. For example, most recycled fibers do not emboss well. Foil stamping is also problematic on these stocks if the surface is abrasive. Recycled papers are more susceptible to cracking when folded.

If you specify recycled stocks, discuss potential pitfalls with your postpress provider. With communication, most recycled papers can be processed without incident.

IMPOSITION

Imposition is the function of positioning pages on printing plates so the press sheets will cut and fold correctly. It is one of the key phases for efficient postpress book production. Imposition is nearly always determined by talking directly with postpress experts — those who work daily overseeing binding and finishing production. They recommend the best folding strategy, and the planner develops the imposition accordingly.

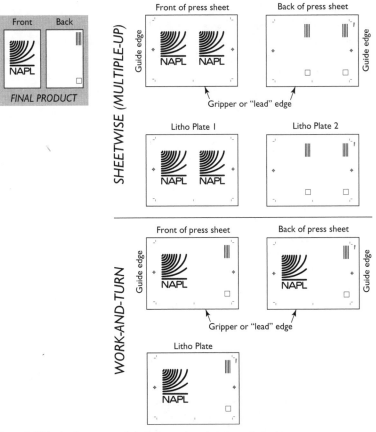

Figure 2-2. The basic concept of sheetwise and work-and-turn imposition.

With an incorrect imposition, the job must be reprinted or alternate production strategies used. Neither are acceptable alternatives.

Flat and folded pieces are imposed differently than bookwork. Flat and folded pieces are imposed either one-up, multiple-up, or ganged (discussed in Chapter 3). When all pieces are positioned on the printing plate face up, it is called a *sheetwise* imposition. This method is very common, and is the only logical choice for one-sided work.

Work-and-turn imposition is another alternative for two-sided work, which places one or more *front* images and one or more *back* images on the same plate. This technique saves plates and makereadies by using the same plate for printing both sides of the paper; the paper is run through the press once, then flipped and run through a second time to print the back of the sheet using the same plates. It is recommended only under specific conditions, where ink drying will not present problems.

Signatures

Book imposition requires placing individual pages in a *signature*, which is a single press sheet that is often combined with other signatures, to create a book. A signature is printed flat, folded, bound with other signatures, and then trimmed on three sides. (The fourth edge is bound with a wire stitch, adhesive, or other binding method). When three sides are trimmed, the sheets are liberated from each other. The binding edge is the only part connecting the loose sheets to each other.

If a book contains sixty-four total pages, sixteen of those pages are printed on a single press sheet and folded in such a way that they end up in proper orientation and sequence. The other forty-eight pages are printed in the same manner on three additional signatures. Four signatures make up the body of this book. They are collated on the stitcher, bound, and trimmed.

An alternative scenario is to print sixty-four pages as eight 8-page signatures. For a number of reasons, smaller signatures may be preferred. If a company has small presses, it may be the only alternative. Better control of registration and color may also be the rationale.

Signatures are used for mass production. It is easier to handle and process four 16-page signatures than thirty-two loose sheets printed on both sides. Four binder pockets can be used instead of thirty-two collator pockets. Saddle-stitched books — where a staple is inserted from the spine to the center spread — can't be produced with individual sheets.

Digital presses, on the other hand, often work with individual sheets and collate on the fly prior to binding. These documents are produced in two-page sheets unless saddle-stitched, in which case they are produced in four-page forms and folded after wire stitching.

Technically, a single signature may be more than one press sheet, as in the case of web offset printing where two or more rolls of paper are

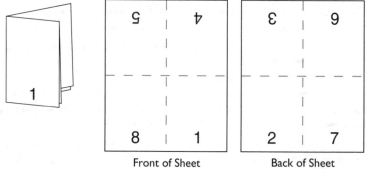

Front of Sheet   Back of Sheet

Figure 2-3. The basic imposition structure for an 8-page signature.

"married" in the folder. We call this a single 32-page signature, although it is made of two press forms.

The 64-page book described earlier was comprised of four 16-page signatures plus a cover. The precise page imposition of each signature is determined using standard templates or making a folding dummy, hand numbering the pages, and then unfolding to see the correct orientation and sequence of the pages. Of course, it is critical that the dummy sheets are folded exactly as they will be in the bindery.

> There are eight different ways to fold a 16-page signature and sixteen ways to fold a 32-page signature. To fold your dummy, you should ask your postpress provider how the actual job will be folded. Although the printing company is responsible for laying out the signatures for optimum production, you can benefit greatly by understanding impositions and signatures.

You may have noticed that signatures are usually multiples of four or eight pages. Although other page counts are possible, common signatures include 4, 8, 12, 16, 24, 32, 48, and 64 pages; most jobs are produced with 4-, 8-, and 16-page signatures.

Books have page counts in multiples of four, eight, or sixteen pages. For example, a book may be sixty-four pages or seventy-two pages, but it is unlikely to be sixty-six pages because production would be inefficient. Saddle-stitched books require page counts in multiples of four, because these books have signatures that cross from the front of the book to the back of the book — two pages in front, two pages in back, and a wire stitch in the middle holding all sheets together.

It is possible to produce a 66-page book by gluing, or *tipping*, a single sheet to another signature. However, it is usually more cost effective to add another two, six, or even fourteen pages to the book to create an even signature. For this reason, many books have blank pages in the back to accommodate productive page counts. You might consider pages for notes in the rear of a book as a creative use of blank pages.

THE DUMMY

The production planner will fold sample signatures to make a dummy. As a designer, you should request one for all book projects. A dummy is a single blank mock-up of your final book. It is usually made of actual stock and replicates the final size and feel of the book, and is an excellent tool to ensure that you like the appearance of the book. Note that dummies are not produced with the same processes as the production book, so dummy bindings may be weak.

Dummies serve four purposes:

1. To determine book thickness (bulking dummy)
2. To check folding accuracy and imposition (folding dummy)
3. To determine book weight for shipping
4. To approve the look and feel, including matching cover papers with book stocks

A *bulking dummy* is used for accurately determining the thickness of a book and spine; actual stock is required. A *folding dummy* is used to determine page imposition and verify the folding sequence; any stock will suffice for the folding dummy. Dummies used for calculating shipping and mailing weights require actual stocks, and should be as close to production weight as possible. Dummies used to help the designer approve the look and feel of the book also require actual stock. These are often used to determine if the cover stock and book paper match in appearance (particularly shade).

CHAPTER 3

CUTTING AND TRIMMING

Most printing jobs require cutting or trimming. Trimming usually implies removing and discarding a small unusable portion of a press sheet, while cutting splits a piece into smaller components. However, few people in the industry actually use these terms exactly; "trimming" and "cutting" are often used interchangeably.

Cutting is used on flat sheets, folded flyers, book signatures, and numerous other products. Cutting is necessary to derive the size and aspect ratio (dimension) of a printed piece. In general, traditional cutting techniques can produce only squares and rectangles. Other shapes — those with straight lines and angles greater than ninety degrees — can also be created using standard cutting methods. If any other shape is needed, die cutting is used (see Chapter 4).

Flat sheets require relatively few postpress operations. Typically, these sheets are cut into smaller units or trimmed to remove scrap. The pieces are then packaged and distributed.

With work that delivers flat, you must consider the stock on which the pieces will print. Flat pieces need enough stiffness to maintain their form. Paper should be selected according to the use of the piece. Postcards, for example, need thickness and stiffness to withstand the equipment of the postal system. Business cards are printed on heavier stock to maintain form when jammed into pockets.

Grain direction may be a concern if the flat piece needs to stand up, be mailed, or if curl may pose a problem. Your printer can advise you on these issues.

CUTTING APPLICATIONS

Most commercial work is printed on oversized sheets and trimmed down to the final size after printing. There are five common reasons for this practice:

1. **Combining two or more of the same image on a larger press sheet.** This technique, called printing *multiple-up*, reduces the number of total sheets to be printed. In other words, if two 8.5 × 11 in. letterheads are printed two-up, printing 2,500 sheets will yield 5,000 pieces of letterhead. Multiple-up is described by the number of pieces on the press sheet — two-up, three-up, four-up, eight-up, and so on.

   If a job will be printed multiple-up, the printer may handle the *stepping* (placement of the duplicate images). You should request that all pieces run with the same grain direction, which is critical for most applications.

2. **Ganging two or more different images on a larger sheet.** *Ganging* is a technique in which two different jobs are printed on the same press sheet. This is commonly used when one job does not fill the press sheet. Using the previous example, if two different letterheads are printed on the same press sheet, more care is required in cutting to track the different pieces.

   Ganging is an efficient way to lower costs, but the separate pieces should not be drastically different. If the design of one is rich with vibrant colors and the other has pastel shades, for example, you may have problems achieving optimum results on both. Ganged jobs often require color sacrifices on press.

3. **Producing a piece that bleeds.** *Bleeds*, or ink that extends off one or more page edges, are the third reason for cutting after the printing. The ink is not printed to the edge of the paper, since it could introduce ink to the backside of the sheet. Rather, the job is printed on an oversize sheet and the paper is trimmed back to the ink.

   When designing bleeds, you need to ensure that bleed elements extend sufficiently past the final trim size. Your bleed margin should extend at least 0.125-in. beyond your final trim. This *bleed margin* allows for minute variances during the cutting operation.

4. **Accommodating the minimum sheet size of a press.** The fourth reason for using an oversized sheet is to accommodate the minimum sheet sizes of a press. If a customer wants business cards, for example, most presses require sheets larger than 2 × 3.5 in.; business cards are one example of a job that is commonly printed on larger sheets.

---

5. **Including control targets for quality printing.** The final reason to print on an oversized sheet is to include quality control targets such as registration marks or color bars, which are used by the printer to ensure accurate registration and ink density. They are later trimmed off and discarded.

CUTTING AND TRIMMING OPERATIONS

The cutting process depends on quality factors such as trim tolerance and tightness of registration, as well as the equipment being used. It is possible to cut and remove trim on some presses, particularly web presses. This reduces cost for high-volume runs, but quality may be sacrificed. A guillotine cutter is the better choice for small-volume jobs.

GUILLOTINE CUTTING

A *guillotine cutter* uses a very large blade that is sliced through a stack of paper with great force. Most are capable of cutting three to four inches of paper in one cycle. This efficient means of cutting and trimming is a quick way to cut large press sheets into many small pieces.

The major components of a guillotine cutter include a side frame, a movable back-gauge for positioning the stock, a clamp for holding the stock in place, and the knife. Proper registration is achieved by ensuring that each sheet is aligned well with the other sheets. After separating the sheets, the operator jogs the stack against the side-frame and the back-gauge, using the same paper edges for registration as those used on press. Next, the clamp is lowered with adequate pressure to completely compress the stack. Too little pressure allows the knife to compress the paper as it cuts, resulting in an uneven cut. Too much clamp pressure leaves excessive marking on the top several sheets of paper.

Knife
Blade   Clamp   Side   Back
                              Frame   Gauge

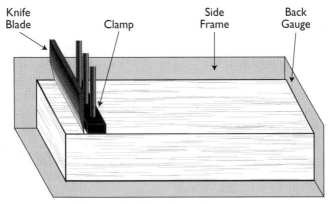

Figure 3-1. The basic elements of a guillotine cutter.

OTHER CUTTING TECHNIQUES

Guillotine cutters are most common for sheetfed work; different cutting techniques are used with other printing applications. When printing from rolls on a web press, rotary slitters are used to slit paper parallel to the running direction, while rotary sheeters cut perpendicular to the running direction. Slitters are also used on folding machines to slit two-up pieces into components.

It is critical that ink dries sufficiently prior to cutting so that the pressures involved won't cause *set-off* (the transferring of ink from sheet to sheet). Certain ink colors take longer to dry than others. Reflex blues, for example, are especially difficult to dry quickly. As a result, some jobs require longer drying times than others before cutting, particularly on coated stock.

DESIGN CONSIDERATIONS FOR CUTTING

When designing a job that requires cutting or trimming, you must consider the exact size and shape the product should take. Generally, squares and rectangle shapes are easier and cheaper than shapes requiring a die or jig.

The primary factors impacting cost for cutting are:

- The type of paper stock
- The layout complexity of the cutting
- Whether or not the design bleeds

Paper is cut in bulk, typically in *lifts* (stacks) of three or more inches. The sheet quantity varies with stock caliper; thinner stocks get more sheets in three inches than thick stocks. Some stocks may also require cutting smaller lift sizes to avoid excessive movement or pressure during the cutting operation. When cutting carbonless forms, for example, high pressure will create marks on the forms.

The layout of your project on a press sheet can affect the efficiency, price, and quality of your job. Typically, the designer provides a digital file containing a single piece. The printer then steps (duplicates and repositions) it to produce two-up, four-up, eight-up, or some variation to maximize the press sheet and running efficiency. The size of the piece and available sheet sizes determine an efficient layout.

An ideal layout generates little, if any, paper waste. In such a case, we achieve 100% paper utilization — all of the paper purchased is delivered in the final product. Several factors, however, prevent this ideal:

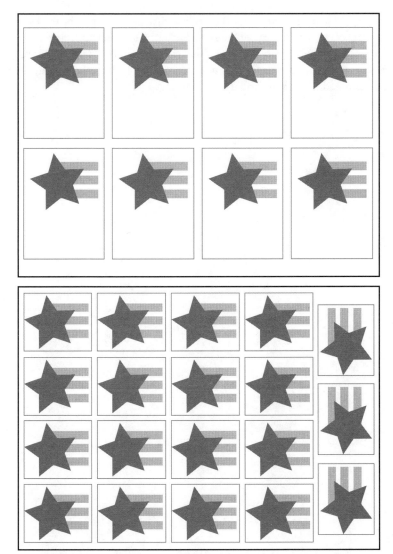

Figure 3-2. These two illustrations show multiple-up layouts. The bottom is a dutch cut, producing pieces with different grain directions.

- Printers put registration marks and color bars on paper for printing, and then trim off the marks prior to delivery.

- If the design bleeds, a final cut is required to achieve the bleed edge.

- The printing press may require that one unprinted edge of the paper be gripped for transport through the press.

All these factors lead to the reality that some paper is wasted in printing. The perfect layout maximizes the press sheet utilization while controlling other quality variables. Maximizing quality may entail running fewer up to maintain register, or using control tools that take up space but are trimmed off and discarded after printing.

CHAPTER 4

DIE CUTTING

Die cutting is used when the straight cuts of a guillotine simply will not achieve the desired shape. Products that require die cutting include cartons, envelopes, pocket folders, items with windows, and complicated promotional pieces, The different methods for die cutting all tend to function like a cookie-cutter, using a shaped knife to outline the paper stock.

Die cutting can make more sophisticated cuts than other cutting processes. These include irregular cuts, cuts that are interior to the edges of a page, carton shaping, and pop-ups. Die cutting can be used for functional as well as decorative purposes. For a pizza box, the die cut produces a three-dimensional, functional box that contains, protects, and insulates the pizza. Die cut tabs in a notebook help in locating content quickly. A pocket folder contains valuable handouts not bound into book form.

Die cutting can also be used for decorative purposes. Die cut windows on reports can enhance the professional appearance of a product. Commercial pamphlets or flyers die cut in the same shape as the product being sold can present a very effective overall message.

WHEN TO USE DIE CUTTING

Die cutting is nearly always more expensive than a guillotine because a special die must be made. Even when a die is on hand, processing the cuts is typically slower. So die cutting is reserved for situations that cannot be served by traditional cutting means — cuts that are not straight. The following situations require cutting with a die:

- Curves
- Angles less than 90º
- Most angles over 90°
- Inside 90º corners
- Removing a window or other cavity from within the paper

If you design a pocket folder, you must build glue tabs into the design to secure the pocket. The glue tabs stick out from the edge of the pocket. Prior to folding and gluing, the piece is cut and scored. The piece cannot cut on a guillotine; it must die cut.

Consider a flat piece shaped as a stop sign. Because the angles are over 90º, it is possible to build a simple jig for the guillotine to cut the edges. The jig is made of wood and allows the operator to align the paper at the proper angle prior to activating the knife. A cost analysis may determine that die cutting is more cost effective, but either method is possible.

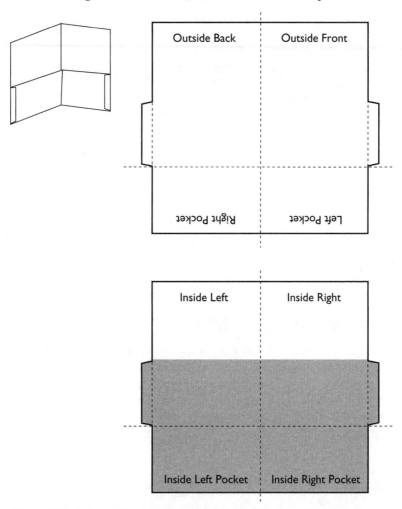

Figure 4-1. The flat layout for a basic pocket folder. The shaded area on the inside will not be visible when the final piece is folded.

If, on the other hand, you intend to create a large flat L-shaped piece, this requires die cutting. Even though all of the angles in an L-shape are 90° and there are no curves or windows, the inside 90° cut (actually 270°) where the two bars connect must be die cut. In this case, a special cutting die is made that functions like a cookie cutter, cutting the entire piece at once.

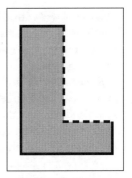

Figure 4-2. Outside cuts (shown as solid lines) can be cut with a guillotine cutter. Inside cuts (shown as dashed lines) require die cutting.

When these complex patterns such as envelopes or cartons are folded, they create nice rectangles that seemingly would work fine on a guillotine cutter. Before these pieces are folded, however, they are complicated patterns and usually require custom dies that match the form of the piece. Since there are literally thousands of different carton types and shapes, nearly every one requires a unique die.

It is useful to crease the stock at the same time it is die cut. For thick stocks such as paperboard, creasing is needed for ease and quality of folding. In a typical job, a carton is die cut around its perimeter and scored where all folds will occur. This is accomplished by combining scoring rule and cutting rule in the same die; the die maker will combine strips of sharp cutting steel with dull scoring steel in the die.

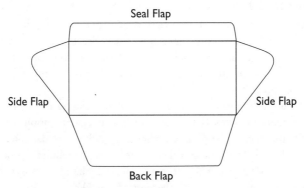

Seal Flap

Side Flap

Side Flap

Back Flap

Figure 4-3. Before being folding to its final form, an envelope must be die cut from the flat press sheet.

DIE CUTTING OPERATIONS

The die cutting process is accomplished in one of several ways. *Steel-rule die cutting* is one of the most common methods, using special plywood called *die board* with thin strips of sharp steel embedded into the board. Steel-rule dies can also be created in rotary form for large boxboard presses; rotary steel-rule dies are more difficult to make, but offer higher processing speeds.

Ram die cutting is similar to a child's Play-Doh® set — The die is open on both ends so a large volume of paper is pushed through the die. Paper is rammed through the die under extreme force, taking the shape of the die. This is the most common method for shaping envelopes, and is used for some glue-applied labels.

Tooled rotary die cutting functions similarly to rotary steel rule, but is a solid base die used on web presses. This method is commonly used on narrow-web label presses with pressure-sensitive stock. The pressure-sensitive material, with a pre-applied adhesive and liner material, is kiss-cut and the waste is stripped in line. *Kiss-cutting*, or cutting only the top layer and not the liner, is frequently used with pressure-sensitive label stock.

Other methods are also used for die cutting. For extremely intricate work, laser cutting can be used. Lasers provide the most elaborate cuts and are used for greeting cards and other unique situations. Laser processing, however, is relatively slow and is used only for very short runs or when the design is so complex that traditional die making is impossible. Other specialty applications of die cutting use heating or ultra-sonic elements to cut unusual materials.

STEEL-RULE DIE MAKING

Steel-rule is the most common type of die cutting, allowing the benefits of quick press makereadies and versatility of use. Steel-rule dies are also less expensive and quicker to make than other die methods. It is used extensively for folding carton, corrugated, point-of-purchase, and commercial products.

Steel-rule cutting can be done in flatbed or rotary form. The dies can be used repeatedly for work that reruns, such as packaging applications. The steel-rule dies need to be replaced when they dull or are damaged, usually by puling the rule from the board without having to rebuild the board.

The die-making process is often completed by hand, although there are automated processes available for various phases. Any combination of steel rules can be used depending on the design. The most common method places a cutting rule around the perimeter of the piece, with interior creasing rules for folding. Depending on the complexity, even a small die may require several hours to complete.

Steel-rule dies are made from 0.5-in. or 0.625-in. plywood die board, which is specially designed to not warp or deform. Steel cutting, scoring, and/or perforating rules are mounted in the board.

A *die line* is transferred to the board, usually by hand. The die maker cuts a thin outline through the board, into which the steel cutting and creasing rules will be inserted. Laser and CNC routers automate this cutting process, and generally produce a more precise die.

Bridges, necessary interruptions in the cut, are required at various locations so the cut shape doesn't fall completely out of the board. These bridges are strategically placed, typically wherever the rule is not well supported. *Notches* are cut in the steel rule to correspond with the bridges.

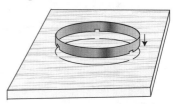

Figure 4-4. A notched cutting rule is inserted forcefully into a die line on the die board.

The strips of steel are cut to length for placement into the die board. After cutting, the rule is notched and bent to shape. The rule is then hammered (carefully but forcefully) into the die board.   0.918 in

The cutting rule's total height is typically 15/16-in. (0.9372 in.), although other heights are available. If the die board is 5/8-in. (0.625 in.) thick, the mounted rule sticks up above the board approximately 5/16-in. (0.3125 in.). A *scoring rule* is a few thousands of an inch shorter than cutting rule, so it doesn't sever the paper completely. The scoring rule is selected based on the caliper of the stock; thicker sheets use a shorter scoring rule while thinner sheets use a taller scoring rule to produce the optimum crease.

After the substrate is die cut, waste needs to be removed. This can be challenging because the sheet should remain in one piece through the die cutting press. If the waste comes off too soon, you have a mess, at best, but more likely the press will jam. To avoid this problem, the die cutter makes *nicks*, or deliberate "flaws" in the cutting rule. These flaws prevent the paper from cutting completely. By strategically placing the nicks along the rule, the die cut window stays connected to its parent until it is intentionally stripped away. The number, size, and placement of the nicks are based on such factors as grain direction, caliper of the paper, and the complexity of the die.

Nicks, while a necessary part of production, can destroy the integrity and appearance of the finished product. A clean, sharp cut is always preferred; nicks result in a slight blemish on the edge of the product. Skilled die cutters are strategic in placing nicks in the die rule, using hidden areas, such as glued flaps or back panels when possible. Unfortunately, it is impossible to entirely avoid placing nicks in noticeable areas.

Steel-rule dies usually cut one sheet at a time. A sheet is fed into the cutting section of the press, where it is aligned to the die; force is then applied and the sheet is cut. Because paper tends to stick in the die, *ejection rubber* is glued to the die at several spots along the rule. This rubber compresses during cutting under the force of the press, but immediately expands and forces the paper away from the die after the cut.

Automating the Process

Various stages of the die-making process can be automated. We already mentioned the role of routers and lasers in cutting the die board. This single improvement offers significant quality advances, because the accuracy of cutting the die board largely dictates the precision of the die. The CAD die line is directly imported into a computer, which drives the machinery in cutting the die board for the rule. Because the file driving the cutting machinery is the same file with which the artwork was built, the die line is cut with exact precision. Many professional die shops have invested in this technology.

Automated rule-processing equipment is a second option for die making. Rule-processing machines cut, notch, and bend the steel rule to shape. Traditional rule-processing involves making a pattern, and then measuring and cutting by hand. The rule is then notched, and is slowly shaped by hand using various patterns and anvils. The fit is tested periodically and modifications are made.

Automated rule processing equipment can produce an accurate rule at a rapid rate. For high-volume operations, automation is necessary for generating the bent rule much more quickly, although the rule must still be mounted into the die board by hand. There is no automated equivalent for mounting steel rule. The precision of automated rule-processing, however, makes the fitting process easier and faster than entirely manual methods.

Steel-Rule Cutting Operation

Steel-rule die cutting is popular for many applications because the dies are cheaper than other forms of die cutting. The process is versatile, working with both sheets and roll stock. Steel-rule can cut many types of material, including paper, plastic, paperboard, and composites.

Much of steel-rule die cutting is done in sheet form, using flat dies and a platen press. The feeder and delivery of the press are similar to a sheetfed lithographic press. The platens are timed to cut the sheet at the fastest possible speed under tremendous pressure.

The die is locked-up in a chase. *Lock-up* describes the process of inserting the die into a metal frame (chase), which is then mounted on the press. Registration in die cutting is as important as registration in printing.

To ensure accurate registration throughout the entire converting process, it is important to know which edge of the sheet was the gripper edge and which was the side guide edge during the printing operation. The same two edges are used through the entire job to register the substrate. Because registration is critical for any postpress operation, press sheets should not be cut before die cutting to ensure that registration control can be maintained throughout.

The makeready process for the die cutter involves getting correct and uniform pressure across the entire die. If pressure is not uniform, one side of the die functions while the other does not. If the pressure is increased, both sides cut but the excessive pressure dulls the knife prematurely.

Stripping involves removing paper waste at the designated time, which can be automated or done by hand. Stripping separates the waste from the good pieces, when transported to the delivery. It is sometimes easier to separate the good pieces and transport the waste through the press, which is called *blanking*. Stripping and blanking are essentially the same process; stripping removes the waste from the press sheet, and blanking removes the finished product from the press sheet.

Some presses incorporate automatic stripping and blanking functions, which requires a wood stripper or blanker form mounted in the press. When needed, these forms are created by the die maker.

RAM DIE CUTTING

Steel-rule cutting forces the sheet into the knife and ejects it back out the same direction. Ram die cutting pushes the stock entirely through the die, ejecting it out the backside. Ram cutting is a fast, efficient production method.

Ram die cutting is popular for applications such as envelopes, which are die cut multiple up. Several dies, placed like puzzle pieces, yield the maximum quantity of envelopes out of a rectangular press sheet. The primary disadvantage of ram cutting is that the dies are expensive. They are deep, precision-tooled pieces of steel that may cost thousands of dollars for even a small die.

Because individual sheets are not positioned to the ram die, registration can be challenging. An entire stack of paper is jogged and the die is focused on the top sheet. If any misalignment occurs, one or more pieces in the stack will be out of register without being detected.

It is common in the glue-applied label business to ram cut labels one-up. The press sheets must be precisely cut down to one-up size on a guillotine cutter, then processed through the ram die. Errors on the guillotine are amplified during die cutting.

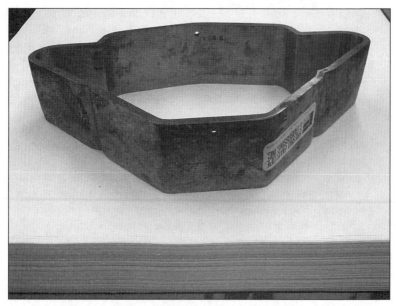

Figure 4-5. Envelopes are commonly cut with a ram die like the one shown here.

Hydraulic or pneumatic pressure is used to produce the force required to push the stock through a ram die. Backpressure helps ensure a clean cut throughout the stack; applying some resistance keeps each sheet flat as it is rammed through the die.

Unlike steel-rule dies, ram dies have no nicks. This results in a cleaner product with no flaws. Stripping is inherent in the process, so removing waste is quite easy.

TOOLED ROTARY DIES

Tooled rotary dies are often used on narrow-web presses. These dies are made of solid steel, from which the pattern is machine- or hand-tooled to create the knives. The substrate is passed between this cutting cylinder and a smooth hard cylinder called an *anvil*. The cutting cylinder pierces the substrate, cutting the material.

Kiss-cutting is an ideal application for tooled rotary dies because the depth of cut can be precisely controlled between the die and the anvil. Cuts are consistent because the dies are machined from a solid piece of steel to precise standards, usually within a couple ten-thousandths of an inch. Rotary dies are generally considered more accurate than either steel-rule dies or ram dies.

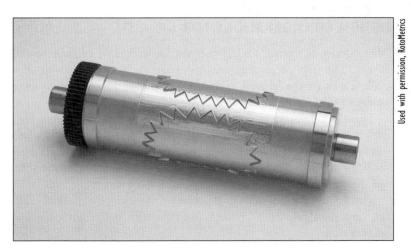

Figure 4-6. Tooled rotary dies are often used on narrow-web presses.

Rotary die cutting is generally faster than steel-rule die cutting. Die cutting of web printed work is usually done inline with the printing, yielding efficient product conversion in one pass. Unlike steel rule dies, tooled rotary dies do not have nicks, resulting in clean product edges.

There are several disadvantages to tooled rotary dies. First, the die is usually more expensive than a comparable rotary steel-rule die. As the die dimensions increase, the cost increases proportionately; tooled rotary dies above 24-in. are uncommon. Narrow-web printers, particularly flexo and gravure label printers, are the primary users of tooled rotary dies. Folding carton printers commonly use rotary or flat steel-rule dies.

Stripping waste can be complex in rotary operations. For pressure-sensitive labels, stripping is relatively easy — as long as all parts of the waste are connected. In this case, the waste is simply peeled away from the release liner and rewound separately from the stock. However, when isolated portions of waste are generated — not connected to other parts, such as windows — the waste can be difficult to remove. With paperboard stock, such as folding carton converting, it can be difficult to strip or blank in rotary form.

Flexible dies have grown in popularity in recent years. These dies are made as a thin flexible metal sheet wrapped around a magnetic cylinder, rather than solid steel. They are less expensive to produce, lighter to ship, and easier to store. These dies can be easily mounted and removed, and offer excellent quality.

DESIGN CONSIDERATIONS FOR DIE CUTS

When designing pieces that die cut, the designer must consider several factors. The first decision is whether a die cut is needed at all. If a guillotine cutter can be used, it should. Die cutting is substantially more expensive than guillotine cutting.

The three primary factors in the cost of die cutting are the size, intricacy, and type of die, along with the speed at which cutting and creasing can be performed. Because intricacy is a significant variable, a small die may cost more than a larger one. A project's budget dictates the role die cutting will play in design, particularly as a decorative tool.

The die maker needs to know the material being cut, the quantity being cut, important press and product quality details, design intricacy, and delivery date.

DIE LINES

When designing a die cut, it is common to generate a die line, a simple line illustration representing the shape of the cut. The die line is made on a separate layer in an illustration program or, for complex packaging, produced in a CAD program. The die maker uses the die line to cut the die board. In many cases, the printer can provide you with a one-up die line for building the artwork.

When creating the die line, similar guidelines to guillotine cutting apply:

- All die elements should be clearly marked, including folds, perforations, cuts, creases, and slits.

- If the project bleeds, bleed elements should extend beyond the die line by at least 0.125 in.

- The die line should be created as a separate layer in an illustration program, which makes it easy to precisely build artwork to the die line.

- The die line should be generated as a 0.25- or 0.5-point line. Designers commonly apply a high-contrast spot color (one not otherwise used in the design) to the line so it is easy to see.

- The die line must be deleted or hidden prior to output so the die line is not printed. If the line is defined with a spot color, it will generate an additional and unwanted separation at output.

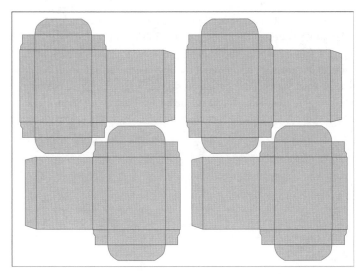

Figure 4-7. Cartons are commonly nested to maximize use of the press sheet.

Certain types of work, such as folding cartons or envelopes, may use elaborate die configurations and nesting strategies to produce the maximum cartons or envelopes on a single sheet. *Nesting* is the technique of stepping the flat shape to fit as many pieces as possible on a sheet. The pieces are nested like a puzzle, fitting parts of one piece into the cavity of another.

Like many aspects of postpress, grain direction is important for ease of folding and structural rigidity. For cartons, grain direction may influence the protective qualities of a package; the grain direction should be consistent on all pieces.

When designing your die cut, consider the complexity of the die line and try to simplify the line. Steel-rule dies have a minimum corner radius of approximately 0.016 in.; corners smaller than the minimum may result in the rule cracking. In most cases, the rule can bend to a greater angle than most people need. If you need a very tight (160° or more) angle, you should discuss the issue with your die maker before proceeding with the design. The die maker can sometimes *broach* the rule, removing a portion of the thickness to increase its ability to bend to extreme angles without cracking.

SUBSTRATE AND COATING SELECTION

You should select a project substrate carefully. Thin stocks, especially in large sheets, are difficult to feed in die cutting presses and should be avoided if possible. Thick stocks are easier than thin stocks to die cut. Dull or matte coated stocks are susceptible to marking or scuffing and should be avoided, or coated on press. The extra expense of sealing the sheet with a dull coating is better than destroying a job with scuff marks.

With folding cartons, die cutting precedes gluing. You should consider the effects of varnishes or on-press coating on glue adhesion. It is important to design your varnish or coating to avoid all glued areas. Some varnishes may allow glue to adhere, but it is safest to simply avoid these areas.

CHAPTER 5

FOLDING

Folding is necessary for many projects, including letters, books, and cartons. Folding is used to accomplish different goals, the most obvious of which is to take a flat piece and create a folded letter or flyer. Another reason is to take advantage of press signatures for bookwork. Rather than gathering single sheets together to process a book, press signatures contain several pages imposed so that when folded, the pages are collated in proper order. In this case, folding serves as the collating tool. By combining several folded signatures together, the entire book's pages are gathered, bound, and trimmed on three sides.

Folding can impact other downstream operations. For example, folding is critical for preparing signatures for saddle-stitching; in such a case, special allowances are added to the folding scheme, as you will see in Chapter 6. Another example of the importance of folding for downstream operations involves mailed pieces. U.S. Postal Service sorting equipment has low tolerance for the method in which mail pieces are prepared (see Chapter 14).

FOLDED FLYERS AND BROCHURES

Flyers and brochures are excellent marketing tools for describing product and company specifications. People use folded brochures because they contain large amounts of information in a compact size. Unlike the flat sheet, folded pieces are small, fitting into a pocket, purse, or display rack.

When designing a flyer or brochure, one of your first considerations is how the document will fold. Common folds include letter (roll), accordion, French or right-angle, gate, and double-parallel. Each offers its own unique benefits.

Each fold provides a different experience for the reader. Some offer a large spread to view a photograph of the product. Others reveal the information one panel at a time. The French fold is commonly used for invitations because it requires only printing on one side.

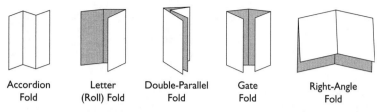

| Accordion Fold | Letter (Roll) Fold | Double-Parallel Fold | Gate Fold | Right-Angle Fold |

Figure 5-1. Five common types of folds.

PANELS, PAGES, LEAVES, AND FLAPS

One of the greatest communication failures occurs when describing panels, pages, and leaves. Books have pages and leaves; folded pieces have panels and flaps.

A *panel* is one front-and-back section of a folded piece. When a panel does not extend as far as the other panels, it is called a *flap*. The common letter fold contains three panels. All folded pieces have at least two unbound panels. Additional panels can be added to increase content. You should think carefully about how to organize your copy so you can take advantage of *spreads* — copy or graphics crossing two or more panels. As the reader unfolds the piece, one or more new panels are revealed. Consider how to maximize impact. Some folded flyers can dramatically reveal four or more panels simultaneously.

Panels and pages are often confused. One panel is equivalent to two book pages. The letter fold has three panels — not six. *Pages* are single-sided sections of a book. This is an important distinction: pages are single-sided while panels are double-sided.

Leaves are single sheets in a book containing two pages. A forty-eight-page book is made of forty-eight pages but only twenty-four leaves. A leaf is actually the same thing as a panel, but the distinction is in the final product — books have leaves and folded pieces have panels. When you communicate with your postpress provider, using accurate terminology will avoid confusion.

FOLDING APPLICATIONS

Folding is important to many printing jobs. Consider a letter designed to fit a #10 envelope. The letter starts out flat. It may be printed one-up, two-up, four-up, or more; it may even be printed on a web press if it is a direct-mail piece. The typical 8.5 × 11-in. letter is letter folded down to 8.5 × 3.75 in.

When two or more folds are parallel to each other, they are called *parallel folds*. When a fold is made perpendicular to the first, it is called a *right-angle fold*. A French fold is an example of a right-angle fold. In general, parallel folds are usually easier to produce, although right angle folds are common.

Folded pieces are usually cut before folding. A typical workflow involves trimming the press sheet into discrete components, which means control marks are removed before folding. The trimmed pieces are loaded onto an automatic folding machine and processed.

Substrate is one of the most significant considerations in folding. Some substrates are easy to fold and others are extremely difficult to fold. Thickness is the primary factor. As a general rule, very thin stocks are easy to fold but difficult to handle through the folding machine; thick stocks are easy to handle and difficult to fold. Each paper thickness requires different techniques to achieve the desired results. The majority of work falls in between these extremes.

Techniques used for folding vary depending on the substrate and the type of fold desired. Folding *sheets* of paper is different from folding *rolls* of paper. Web presses, which print from roll stock, frequently have in-line folding capabilities, where the substrate is folded directly after printing. In most cases, web presses have fewer folding options but operate at higher speeds and produce the bulk of high-volume, long-run work. Sheetfed work is commonly folded off-line after printing. The sheets are transported from the pressroom to the bindery for processing and packaging.

Scoring, or creasing the sheet before folding, may be required in order to produce a clean fold, especially for cover and paperboard stocks. Book and bond stocks generally do not need scoring, although thick book stocks with heavy ink coverage may benefit from scoring.

When a sixteen-page signature is folded, bulkiness occurs along the head and spine, especially during the third fold. *Perforating* signatures is a common practice in folding operations. Stress on the paper is relieved by perforating at the head (top) or fore (the edge opposite the spine) edges, allowing the air to escape, the paper to flex, and the signature to compress.

Perforating, however, weakens the paper. Care is taken to perforate only in spots that achieve the desired results but don't sacrifice strength. For saddle-stitched books, perforating the spine edge would negatively affect book strength. On the other hand, perforating on the spine is common for perfect bound books. Because the spine is ground off, the perforation doesn't impact book strength and, in some cases, enhances it. Perforated signatures are nipped and smashed to create a flatter book.

FOLDING OPERATIONS

Sheet folding is accomplished in several ways. For very short runs, hand folding is one possible alternative. More commonly, folding is achieved using a buckle folder, knife folder, inline folder/gluer, or rotary inline folder. Each of these has unique applications.

BUCKLE FOLDING

The buckle folder is used for many commercial products because of its extreme versatility — capable of hundreds of folding combinations. It can be used with most stocks, except heavy paperboards.

The buckle fold is accomplished by forcing paper against a stop, causing the paper to buckle and crease at the fold. The precise location of the fold is easily controlled by the stop position. Two nip rollers are located where the paper buckles, to crease the paper at the fold and transport it to the next buckle stop or delivery. By increasing the paper feed into the buckle plate, the first panel gets longer. Shortening the paper feed reduces the size of the first panel.

Multiple folds can be achieved by positioning successive buckle sections. Most buckle folders have four or more buckle sections in a row. Two buckle plates are positioned up and two are positioned down. An *up* buckle plate folds by lifting up the edge of the sheet; a *down* buckle plate folds by taking down the edge of the sheet. Four parallel folds can be made in each section — two up folds and two down folds. Most jobs do not require all four plates, but any combination can be used to get the desired fold.

Folding machines are often equipped with one or more additional sections called right-angle sections. These detachable units offer four additional buckle plates, perpendicular to the previous section. The first right-angle section is often called an 8-page section, because the first right-angle fold produces an 8-page signature. In this case, the first buckle plate in the main section is used along with the first buckle plate in the 8-page unit. The first plate in the 8-page section is also referred to as the fifth buckle plate.

If a second right-angle section is added, it is called a 16-page section and folds at a right angle to the 8-page section. A 32-page unit may also be added. It would be impossible to use all buckle plates in each of these sections, but their availability increases versatility.

Anytime a right-angle fold is used, the paper path changes directions. In other words, an 8-page signature momentarily stops after the first fold, and is then redirected in a perpendicular direction to the original path. To fold a 16-page signature, it is stopped again and redirected into the next right-angle section.

It is common to fold simple pieces two-up, and then separate them by slitting at the folder. Using this technique, rather than cutting a sheet down to single items and then folding, the sheet is cut to a two-up size. The result is two streams of folded product off a single folder. This practice is common for large quantities of simple work. It can be done with jobs that bleed, although it is simplest with work that does not bleed.

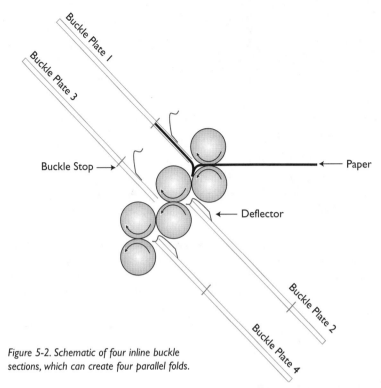

Figure 5-2. Schematic of four inline buckle sections, which can create four parallel folds.

There are many ways to fold a sheet of paper and end up with the same results. Something as simple as an 8-page signature, for example, can be folded in the following ways: Buckle plates 1 and 5; 1 and 6; 2 and 5; and 2 and 6. Each of these four methods results in a different page order, so the correct signature imposition relies on knowing exactly how the signatures will be folded.

The direction of the buckle plates being used (up or down) affects the final page order. Using plates 1 and 5, the sheet is folded up, and then up again at a right angle. Using plates 1 and 6, the sheet is folded up, and then *down* at a right angle. One might think that the folding will simply adapt to the imposition, but in practice, production variables can make one folding method preferable over another.

KNIFE FOLDING

Knife folding is another method of folding. A dull knife is used to crease and force the paper into a set of nipper rollers, which grab the paper and transport it to the delivery or another folding section.

One advantage of knife folding is the reduction of ripple cracks. When paper is bent beyond its point of elasticity, ripple cracking occurs. This

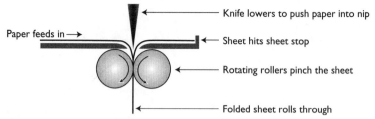

Figure 5-3. Basic schematic of a knife folding mechanism.

happens as a result of the extreme stresses that are applied to the paper during buckle folding — particularly on stocks thicker than 10 points, or 0.010 in. These cracks appear parallel to the fold, approximately 0.5 in. from the fold, and can crop up even with scored stocks. Knife folding does not apply the same forces that cause ripple cracks.

It is common for a knife folder to be combined with buckle plates in the first unit, because buckle plates are very efficient for parallel folds. The first fold is achieved using a buckle plate. Then, rather than changing paper directions (which limits the folder's speed), a knife folder creates the right-angle fold.

One disadvantage of the combination knife folder is that buckle folders are typically faster in production settings. The cyclical action of the knife simply cannot keep up with buckle folding.

INLINE FOLDING/GLUING

Inline folder/gluers are used for paperboard boxes, cartons, pocket folders, and similar products. The inline folder uses plows to fold the stock, which puts less stress on the paper. Because of paperboard thickness, in-line equipment folds the scored substrate gradually as the product is conveyed down the line. Most die-cut items are folded on inline folder/gluers since their unusual shapes would be impossible to feed on other folder types.

Inline folders are equipped with one or more gluing units. Glue is applied on flaps of a product during folding. As the folds are made, the glued piece makes contact with its complementary section. Inline folder/gluers deliver products that are glued, folded, and delivered flat. When filled, they are expanded and the tops and bottoms are sealed.

Pocket folders are often folded and glued on this type of equipment. When large numbers of inserts are desired, capacity pocket folders are produced. When a pocket has capacity —three-dimensional to insert a large number of sheets — it is usually folded and glued by hand, which is more expensive than automated methods.

ROTARY INLINE FOLDING

Web presses often have in-line folding capabilities, where the folding is done in combination with the printing. Newspaper, magazine, and commercial web presses all have folders as part of their finishing equipment. Folding capabilities are more limited, but web press folders are excellent at producing common products such as magazines or catalogs at a high rate of speed.

A typical folder for commercial web printing is a combination folder. A combination folder folds four common product sizes:

- Broadsheet (e.g., newspapers such as *USA Today*)

- Tabloid (e.g., half-size newspapers such as *National Enquirer*)

- Quarter-fold (e.g., commercial magazines such as *Time* or *Newsweek*)

- Double-parallel or double-digest fold (e.g., small magazines such as *TV Guide* and *Reader's Digest*)

One final comment is important about folding on commercial web offset presses. Most commercial presses have fixed cutoffs. Although roll widths can be changed, the cutoff dimension of the paper is a fixed size and never changes. You should discuss this with your printer to see if efficiencies can be gained by slightly altering product size.

DESIGN CONSIDERATIONS FOR FOLDING

When designing folds, the key considerations are selecting the best fold, accounting for gutter space, making a folding dummy, providing appropriate marks, and addressing crossovers.

FOLD SELECTION

All folded pieces contain panels. Content can be increased by adding additional panels; a minimum folded piece contains two panels. Consider a three-panel accordion fold. Additional content can be added by making it a four-panel accordion fold. This, of course, changes the flat piece size, and may alter the press sheet dimensions and efficiency.

There are literally thousands of different methods and types of folds. The most common folds are roll, double-parallel, right-angle, accordion, and gate. Your job is to select the fold that enhances the reader experience and maximizes the impact of your message.

Roll Fold

Roll folding involves rolling three or more panels in on each other in a successive manner. The simplest roll fold is the letter fold. As the number of panels increase, the product becomes bulkier and more difficult to fold. In general, no more than five panels are roll folded (particularly with thicker stocks).

Roll folds are designed with internal panels smaller than exterior panels to accommodate paper thickness. Only the outside two panels are sized to the final dimension. All other panels are reduced in size to compensate for paper caliper, ensuring that sufficient paper is removed from each panel to achieve a clean fold. Inside panels should typically be 1/16-in. smaller than the panel enclosing it, although thicker paper may require additional trim allowance.

Roll folds are useful for reducing larger sheets to fit in a pocket or #10 envelope. The finished product offers a front panel for display in a rack, and can be successively unrolled to reveal more content. Panels are revealed one at a time, making roll folds useful for consecutive content. When flat, the panels present a spread for larger photographs.

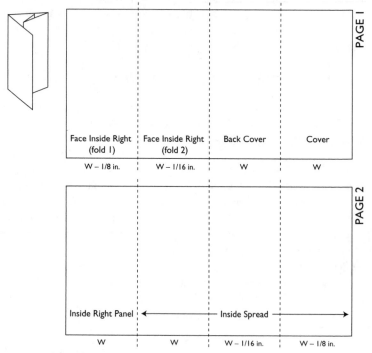

Figure 5-4. The page setup for a four-panel roll fold (W = finished width).

Double-Parallel Fold

Double-parallel folds involve folding a sheet in half, and then in half again with the folds parallel to each other. Their format and size are similar to a four-panel roll fold, but the double-parallel fold provides a slightly different user experience. Like the roll fold, the cover displays well in a rack. When opened, however, two additional panels are revealed to the user rather than one. Finally, all four panels are revealed simultaneously.

As with the roll fold, the designer must consider panel size when designing double-parallel folds. The inside panels have a tendency to extend beyond the desired trim edge, called *creep*. Inside panels should be fractionally smaller than outside panels to compensate for this problem.

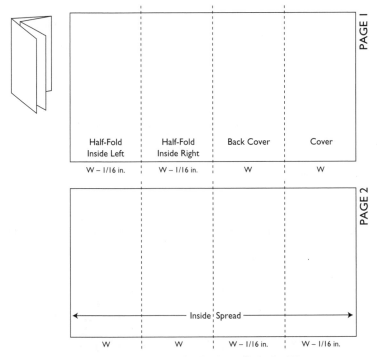

Figure 5-5. The page setup for a double-parallel fold (W = finished width).

Accordion Fold

In an accordion fold, each panel is doubled back in a "Z" pattern; these folds zig-zag back and forth. No panel is folded inside another one, so no size compensation is needed for accordion folds. Like the roll and double-parallel folds, the accordion fold displays well and can be made to fit in a pocket or envelope. The user experience with an accordion fold is slightly

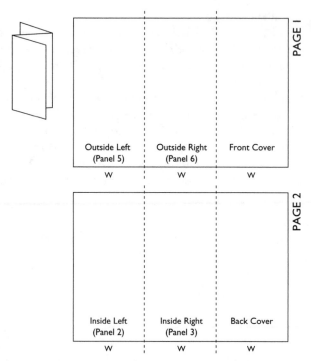

		PAGE I
Outside Left (Panel 5)	Outside Right (Panel 6)	Front Cover
W	W	W

		PAGE 2
Inside Left (Panel 2)	Inside Right (Panel 3)	Back Cover
W	W	W

Figure 5-6. The page setup for an accordion fold (W = finished width).

different from the roll or double-parallel fold. Few people treat each panel individually; most expand the piece from the start and read it flat. All content is revealed from the beginning. Long blocks of text can span several panels.

Gate Fold

Gate folds have two or more panels folding into the center from opposing sides. The reader experience is similar to the double-parallel fold, with the piece first opening to a two-page spread, and then finally to a four-page spread.

Gate folds need a *gate gap* of at least 1/16 in. where the two gate panels meet,

> A gate fold is one of the more difficult folds to produce. Postpress companies frequently charge a small premium for gate folds because the machinery runs more slowly.

which means that each inside panel must be 1/32 in. smaller than the two outside panels. This gap is necessary to prevent the gates from crimping when the fold is closed. This gap limits crossovers and reveals the content of the center spread.

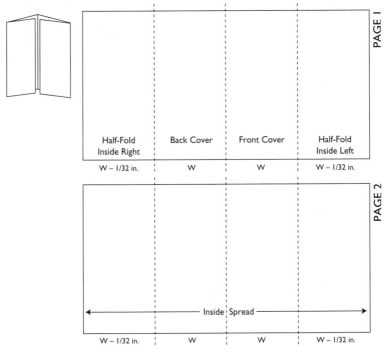

Half-Fold Inside Right	Back Cover	Front Cover	Half-Fold Inside Left
W – 1/32 in.	W	W	W – 1/32 in.

PAGE 1

PAGE 2

◄──────────────── Inside Spread ────────────────►

W – 1/32 in.	W	W	W – 1/32 in.

Figure 5-7. The page setup for a gate fold (W = finished width).

Right-Angle Fold

Right angles fold a sheet in half, and then in half again with the second fold perpendicular to the first. A third fold at a right-angle to the second can be added to produce more panels. These folds are very common for book signatures where three sides are trimmed, but are not as frequently used for other folded commercial work. Some designers use an eight-page right-angle fold (also called a French fold), for invitation work, the advantage of which is the ability to print only one side of the sheet and fold it into an invitation.

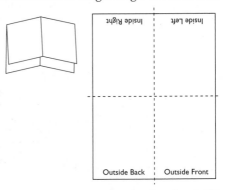

Inside Right	Inside Left
Outside Back	Outside Front

Figure 5-8. The page setup for a French fold. These are typically printed on only one side, so there is no Page 2 layout.

FOLDING DIAGRAM

Before sending your work to the printer, you should make a folding dummy, which will be used to demonstrate to the postpress professional the exact folding sequence. As an alternative to a dummy, some designers use a drawn diagram to indicate folding sequence. In this type of diagram, it is customary to draw each panel on a sheet and label the first fold "A", the second fold "B", and so on.

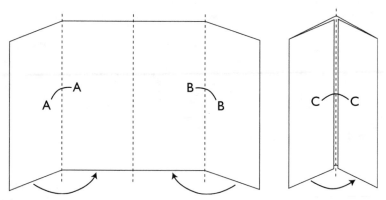

Figure 5-9. The folding sequence for a gate fold.

GUTTER SPACE

When designing a piece that folds, you need to consider the appropriate margins for each panel. It is a common novice mistake to provide a 0.5-in. margin between each panel as well as the outside borders. This actually results in a 0.5-in. margin on the outsides, but only 0.25-in. margin for each inside panel. Consider each panel individually when allocating margin space.

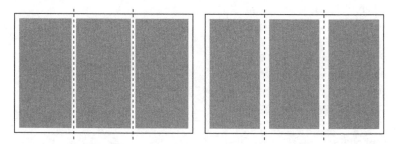

Figure 5-10. Many beginning designers apply the same margin between columns, resulting in only half the margin width for each panel (shown left). Margins should be even for all four sides of individual panels (shown right).

Before you submit a file to the printer, it is wise to output the project on your desktop printer at 100% size, tiled if necessary. If you cannot print both sides on your printer, output the front and back separately, and then tape them together in register. Next, fold the piece at the correct location to make sure that the images are centered on each panel and the product folds correctly. Beginning designers skip this step, and sometimes end up with inaccurate panel size and placement.

FOLD MARKS

It is important to prepare your artwork with appropriate marks to identify the exact location of the folds, which ensures that the folds will be precisely placed during the folding operation. Fold marks are usually identified with a dotted or solid line in the non-image portion of the artwork, and can be used by the folder operator for reference.

You can create these marks by drawing a 0.5-in. dotted line at the location of the desired fold. To appear in the final output, any elements must at least touch the live page area of the design. The fold line should be placed so it touches the live page area, and then covered with a white or "paper" colored box to prevent the fold line from printing inside the trim area.

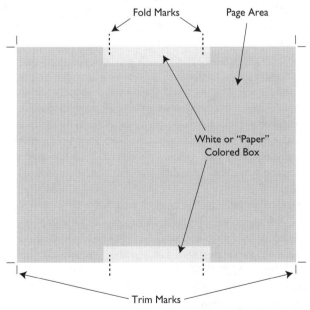

Figure 5-11. In a page-layout application, fold marks should extend slightly into the page area, then be covered by a white or "paper" colored box (shown here as a lighter shade for illustration purposes).

DESIGNING CROSSOVERS

One of the most important ways a designer can influence quality is with the production of *crossovers*. Crossovers are image elements that cross from one page to the next, spanning the gutter of the book or panels on a folded piece. Two side-by-side pages are called a spread; crossovers span one or more spreads. Since adjacent pages in a book are frequently imposed on different parts of the signature — or even an entirely different signature — folding influences the seamless appearance of crossovers.

The first step in designing a crossover is to place a copy of the image on both pages. Each copy of the image is then cropped to only include the portion of the image that

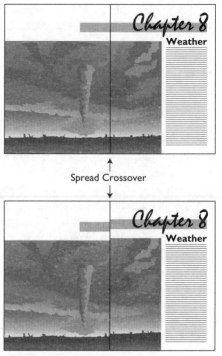

Figure 5-12. The appearance of crossovers can be ruined if folding is not within a specific tolerance.

appears on the corresponding page. With perfect binding, you need to also incorporate 0.125-in. overlap that is ground off at the spine.

The best method for achieving a clean crossover is to create two distinct files in an image-editing program. You should crop the image appropriately for each page (including the 0.125-in. overlap for perfect binding, if necessary), and then save and import the separate files into the page layout.

Understanding the job's imposition may help to ensure high-quality crossovers. If both pages of a crossover fall on one side of a signature, you can be confident that each half of the crossover will appear consistent. If your crossover pages are positioned on separate signatures or different sides of the same signature, they will likely be produced as separate press runs, increasing the chances that the color will vary slightly. In this case, you should discuss your concerns with your printer.

It is common design practice to place a thin line or keyline that crosses over a spread. While this may be visually pleasing, it is a folding challenge to execute these tight crossovers. Any lines or sharp breaks are difficult —

though not impossible — to match perfectly as a crossover. You should work with your printer and postpress professional to minimize the difficulties. These experts can advise you in stock selection and laying out the job to maximize success.

If you decide to use thin lines or another challenging crossover, you should discuss the acceptable tolerance for your project. It is impossible to produce perfectly aligned crossovers at production speeds; ±1/32-in. is a generally accepted tolerance. Tolerances are a necessary part of communicating your expectations with your postpress professional. For very difficult crossovers, parallel folded signatures may be used for better accuracy.

SUBSTRATE SELECTION AND SCORING

Nearly all papers can be folded. Some papers, however, fold with greater ease than others. Thick or stiff papers may require off-line scoring before folding. Cover stocks usually require channel scoring, the process of using dull scoring rule and a channel — functioning as a counter die — to crease a sheet before folding. Most book and bond stocks can be folded without scoring.

Several factors influence a paper's ability to fold cleanly, including grain direction. The printer will usually try to place your design on the press sheet so the paper grain is parallel to the folds. Because of size discrepancies, greater efficiencies are sometimes achieved by laying out the

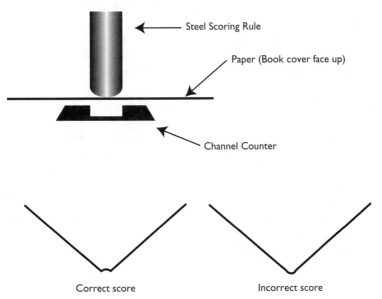

Steel Scoring Rule

Paper (Book cover face up)

Channel Counter

Correct score   Incorrect score

Figure 5-13. Channel scoring may be required, especially for book covers.

press sheet so the stock folds against the grain. Discuss this with your printer to see if benefits can be achieved by altering your image size slightly. Even a 0.25-in. change of each panel might allow the piece to fold with the grain instead of against it, which will save significant money if it eliminates the need for off-line scoring.

Designers frequently select a product size without considering available paper sizes. Paper is available in standard sizes; efficiencies can be gained by ensuring that waste is minimized. It may be possible to alter panel sizes very slightly and achieve significant cost savings.

Synthetic stocks are beneficial for their ability to withstand high-moisture environments, as well as resist tearing. *Memory*, a stock's desire to return to a flat state, may be a problem in folding synthetic stocks. Discuss your needs with your postpress professional before proceeding with synthetic paper.

Dull and matte stocks have the potential for scuffing or marking in the folder. This problem can be avoided by selecting a different stock, or applying a varnish or coating on press. Your supplier can provide advice and suggestions for minimizing the scuffing potential of dull and matte stocks.

PRESS-APPLIED COATINGS

Press-applied coatings and varnishes are important for resisting scuffing or marking. However, when folded, the varnished sheets can be difficult to feed because of their slipperiness, particularly if a high amount of static is also present. Coatings and varnishes don't always apply smoothly. As the sheets are sent through the folder, the varnish or coating begins to lose some pigment particles, which end up coating the folding rollers and cause inaccurate folds. To correct these problems, the postpress operator periodically stops and cleans the rollers; a typical job that runs at 9,000 pieces per hour, for example, might fold at 5,000 if varnished. Your printer may be able to provide substrate or coating recommendations to avoid this problem.

Designing with the environment in mind is certainly an important goal. As noted in Chapter 2, recycled papers do not perform as well in postpress as virgin fiber paper. When paper is recycled, the fibers are broken and shortened in the process. Shorter fibers have greater abrasive characteristics and tend to crack more frequently when folded. These stocks will require scoring more frequently than virgin fiber. Recycled stock is also more subject to jams on folding equipment, and higher waste may result.

CHAPTER 6

SADDLE-STITCHING

INTELLIGENT BINDING CHOICES

Bookbinding is an excellent way to illustrate the range of choices available for postpress. Many different binding methods are available, each providing its own advantages and user experience.

Books, or any product with multiple pages, require a means to secure the pages in sequence and allow the reader to leaf through the pages as needed. Ultimately, you (or your client) must specify which binding method will be best for a given product. A thorough knowledge of the options makes this decision easier, and results in a more effective product.

There are four broad categories of book bindings:

- **Wire Stitching.** Wire stitching uses staples to hold several sheets together. It is called stitching because the process does not use preformed staples. Rather, the stitch is formed from a coil: cutting the wire, forcing it through the paper, and shaping the legs. Because book thickness varies from job to job, a preformed staple is not practical. The stitch shape is dictated for the book caliper — long legs for thick books and short legs for thin books.

- **Adhesive Binding.** Adhesive binding uses glue to secure one edge of several pages to a cover. Perfect binding is the most common form of adhesive binding. The binding edge is roughened through a grinding process so the adhesive can

Books are described by their page count and the type of cover. A *self-cover* book means the cover is printed on the same basis-weight stock as the body. A *plus-cover* book means the cover is a separate stock, always a heavier and thicker substrate. "64-page plus cover" means there are 64 pages on one paper and four additional cover pages on a heavier stock. A 64-page self-cover means there are 60 pages printed on the same paper as the 4-page cover. There are sixty-four total pages on the same stock, not sixty-eight.

penetrate into the paper, forming a strong bond. The cover is applied shortly after the adhesive and secured through a nipping or squeezing process.

- **Mechanical Binding.** Mechanical binding is a broad term that encompasses several binding techniques, including comb, Wire-O®, spiral coil, ring, and Velo® binding. A common theme among these techniques is a piece of metal or plastic that serves to secure the pages together. In all of these cases, holes are punched and a metal or plastic securing device is threaded through the holes.

> The term "mechanical binding" implies using tools to hold the sheets together in a mechanical way. You could make the case that a wire stitch should fit into this category, but its popularity puts it into a category of its own.

- **Case Binding.** Case binding is what we commonly think of as a book with a hard cover. The body pages may actually be secured in a variety of different manners. A case can be put onto a thread-sewn body, a perfect-bound body, a side-wire-stitched body, or some other technique. Case binding simply implies securing a paperboard case around the book to protect its pages.

SELECTING THE BEST METHOD

Common considerations for selecting a book binding method include:

- Cost of production

- Durability, including life expectancy, frequency, and type of use

- Physical appearance

- Ease of use for the reader

- Page count/thickness of book body

When selecting your binding method, you should first consider the nature of the book. The physical appearance of your book is largely determined by the binding method used. What image are you trying to portray?

Each book has particular needs. Some books, such as a yearbook, an encyclopedia, reference books, or a Bible, are intended to last a lifetime. These books will be opened and closed many times, so they need durable binding spines. A weekly automobile trader magazine is probably thrown away after one or two readings, so the binding is typically designed for single-use.

Some books are stored on shelves in a manner that shows their spines. Some books are displayed on a coffee table. Others are stacked in a magazine rack and are discarded after reading. How important is printing a title on the spine? Again, it depends on the type of book.

Next, analyze the expectations of your audience, which goes hand-in-hand with the purpose of the book. If your reader anticipates a particular quality, such as a limited-edition volume, a saddle-stitched or perfect-bound book will be disappointing.

Another significant factor in your selection is the life expectancy of the product. The product with the shortest lifespan is probably the daily newspaper. This product is not bound at all; it is handled so little that when it gets jumbled, the effects are not devastating. Contrast this with a family Bible, designed to last for decades. It must withstand being opened, used, closed, stored, and used again — all the time looking elegant. The typical family Bible is case bound with a hard or leather cover. It should last an extended period without losing pages; it should lie flat; and it must protect the interior pages.

When selecting a binding method, page count, and specifically the thickness, are of prime importance. In fact, the thickness may well eliminate certain choices for you. Mechanical binding methods can accommodate a wide range of book sizes and thicknesses. Wire stitching is usually reserved for thinner books and magazines, while perfect binding and case binding are reserved for thicker volumes. Saddle-stitching is limited to books that are less than 0.25 in. thick. When your book gets above this caliper, saddle-stitching is no longer an option.

Because selecting your binding method is such an important process, many factors are considered in deriving the best solution.

SADDLE-STITCHING APPLICATIONS

Saddle-stitching is a wire stitching method where a staple is used to secure the pages of a book to a paperback cover. Technically, it is not stapling because the wire is formed during the stitching process; *stapling* uses preformed wire.

Saddle-stitching is one of the few binding methods that secures the sheets from the back to the middle of the book. It inserts the wire in the spine and crimps it at the center spread. Since the wire originates from the spine rather than the front, no obtrusive device detracts from the cover design. Saddle-stitching is one of the few methods that cannot easily take a single leaf, because of the need to wrap the sheet from the front of the book to the back of the book for binding.

Saddle-stitching is popular for a variety of reasons. It is relatively fast, inexpensive, and attractive. These books lie flat, aiding the reading process, and are reasonably durable. Saddle-stitched books are not intended to last forever so if the binding does fail, it is usually beyond the life of the book. Saddle-stitching is a high-speed process, so books can be produced quickly at low cost. For small books in large-volume, binding can be preformed two-up and trimmed after stitching to increase productivity.

Saddle-stitching is used for producing both short-run and long-run books with low page counts. Magazines, catalogs, brochures, pamphlets, calendars, and circulars are all commonly saddle-stitched because there are few other high-speed methods for low-page-count books.

An alternative to saddle-stitching is side-stitching. It involves using a wire stitch that inserts in the front and exits out the back of the book. The common stapler is often used in this manner. Side-stitching has two primary downfalls. First, the stitch is visible on the front of the book — a detracting feature. Second, side-stitched books do not lie flat when opened.

On occasion, you may see side-stitching combined with other binding methods. For example, some magazines side-stitch the body pages and then perfect bind the cover to them. The wire stitches are hidden by the perfect-bound cover. This adds strength and increases the binding life.

SADDLE-STITCHING TECHNOLOGY

Saddle-stitching works with folded signatures, where one is inserted inside another. The wire is stitched through the spine, and the product is finished with a three-knife trim. If the project includes a cover, it is applied as the outside signature.

Most high-speed stitchers serve three or more functions; collating, stitching, and trimming are performed in line. Additional functions may include scoring, folding a cover, carton packing, or applying ink-jet labeling for mailing.

POCKETS

Before a job gets to the collator/stitcher/trimmer, the signatures are printed and folded. The signatures are placed on skids or strapped in a form called a *log* for transportation to the binding line. Signatures must be kept organized so that they are placed in the proper collating pocket. Any mix-up in signatures results in defective books.

The collator/stitcher/trimmer has a given number of pockets, which predetermines the total signatures that can be included in the book. If a stitcher has six pockets, then six signatures can be in the book on a single pass. If each of those six signatures is 16 pages, then the book can be up to 96 pages plus a cover. If the job is run in 8-page signatures, then the stitcher can produce a 48-page book. Press limitations, folder limitations, or other factors may dictate the page count of signatures.

Each stitcher pocket contains a unique signature, which is opened and dropped onto a saddle or chain. The open signature straddles the chain, with half of the book in front and half in the back. The chain moves to the next pocket, where the next signature is opened and placed on top of the previous one. The cycle continues down the binding line until each signature has been placed on the preceding one; the first pocket contains the center pages, and the last pocket contains a signature with half low-numbered pages and half high-numbered pages.

SELECTIVE BINDING

Magazine publishers may have ten or more pockets on their saddle-stitchers. Companies that produce magazines and catalogs use a technique called *selective binding*. Selective binding involves producing targeted, demographic advertising in magazines, including specific ads for specific individuals. For example, stitcher pockets 7, 8, and 9 may contain discreet signatures that include the same editorial pages but different advertisements.

If a single magazine ends up with more than one of these targeted signatures, the magazine is defective. Selective binding is tied electronically to a database that instructs the binding line to initiate only one of the pockets based on the demographics of the reader. Other signatures are skipped for this book. As each magazine is made, the database is consulted to determine which advertisements to include in the magazine for a given individual.

BINDING LAP

To set the signatures on the chain, they are opened either mechanically or pneumatically. The easiest method is to include a *gripper lap* (sometimes called lip) on the signature for mechanical opening with gripper fingers. The terms lap and lip are used interchangeably in the industry.

The gripper lap is created by extending the fore-edge of the front half of the signature (called a *low-folio lap*) or the back half of the signature (called a *high-folio lap*) approximately 0.375 in. beyond the other.

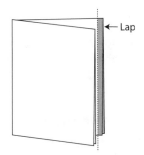

Figure 6-1. A high-folio lap extends the fore edge of pages 5–8 in a folded 8-page signature.

Lap location dictates whether the signatures will align at the head or foot during processing. Bindery personnel usually specify high- or low-folio laps based on how the signatures will be jogged or aligned. Inserted reply cards may need to jog to the head, dictating a high-folio lap for all signatures. Consistency is critical; all laps must be either in the front or in the back.

The stitcher grippers use the lap to open the signature. Although laps are the preferred method, a signature without laps can still be opened and placed on the saddle using suction. This is only possible with right-angle signatures with closed heads or feet (before the signature is trimmed to separate the pages), generally produced as 8- or 16-page folds. Double-parallel signatures cannot be opened with vacuum since they do not have closed heads or feet; they require a lap.

When laying out signatures, a prepress technician will decide whether a lap will be included in the press sheet layout, or if vacuum will be used on the stitcher. If a lap is needed, the press sheet layout must provide sufficient room for the extra paper needed by the stitcher grippers. A folded dummy is an easy way to determine the location and size of the lap.

COVERS

After all pockets have distributed signatures on the saddle, the signatures are transported to the cover feeder, where a flat, soft cover is scored, folded, and dropped on the chain. At this point, the book is collated and ready for wire stitching. Most stitching machines perform a quick caliper check to determine if the book thickness is correct; if not, the signatures are ejected from the saddle.

A score is made at the cover feeder with a rotary scoring wheel, which is adequate for many covers but does not produce the same quality as a steel-rule channel score. Heavy cover stocks may need a better score because of the nature of the paper and the coverage of the ink. Coated papers have a greater potential for cracking than uncoated stocks. Thick, coated cover stocks should be tested early in the process.

The amount of ink applied at the spine is perhaps more important than the stock itself. Ink can crack, revealing noticeable white fibers. Ink coverage is a primary factor in determining whether a cover needs offline channel scoring.

STITCHING HEADS

After the signatures and cover are collated, the book is stitched. The wire used in saddle-stitching is supplied in coil form, which allows for varying the stitch length as book calipers change. The stitching head straightens and forms the wire on the bender block. The wire is cut, the driver forces the stitch through the book, and the legs are clinched and bent, completing the process.

Books with two stitches and three stitches are common, although other options are possible. For most circumstances, two stitches provide enough strength to secure the pages. Three stitches are used in situations where the book is expected to receive excess handling or abuse.

Small books, which may be produced two-up, require four stitching heads. The press sheet is laid out so that the product folds to the two-up signature size. After four stitches are applied, the books are split apart in the trimming section.

LOOP STITCHING

The loop stitch is a variation of the tradition stitch. This method is used when producing resale product catalogs, which are often inserted into large three-ring binders at the merchant's store. Loop stitching is an alternative to drilling three holes through the pages of a catalog. If a catalog highlights photographs, these holes can be distracting — particularly when the layout includes large crossovers. The loop stitch facilitates ring inserting without drilling holes.

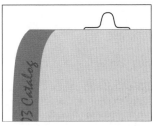

Figure 6-2. A loop stitch is often used to avoid drilling holes into three-ring binder catalogs.

THREE-KNIFE TRIMMING

After the wire stitches have been inserted, the book moves to the trimming section, where the three unbound sides are trimmed. When signatures are saddle-stitched, they have closed head and fore edges. These need to be removed so the sheets are separate and free to turn. A second reason for trimming is to ensure all edges are smooth, creating a polished look.

Approximately 0.125 – 0.5 in. is trimmed off the three non-spine edges. Bleeds are incorporated in this trim margin. The prepress technician imposes the press sheet layout to include trim area on each page.

When books are produced two-up, a four- or five-knife process is used to split the two books apart. One long knife trims the fore edge of both books, then a three- or four-knife section trims the feet and heads of both books. Five-knife trimming is necessary when all edges of the book contain bleeds; two knives are used to split the books, removing the bleed trim.

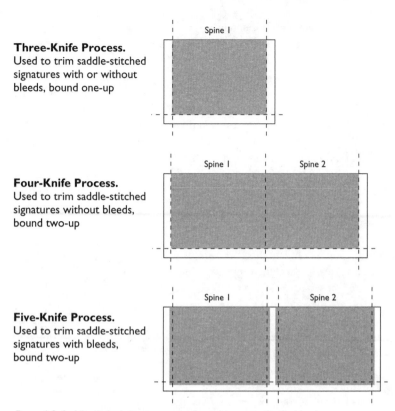

Three-Knife Process.
Used to trim saddle-stitched signatures with or without bleeds, bound one-up

Four-Knife Process.
Used to trim saddle-stitched signatures without bleeds, bound two-up

Five-Knife Process.
Used to trim saddle-stitched signatures with bleeds, bound two-up

Figure 6-3. Saddle-stitched signatures are trimmed to create the final book. The dotted lines indicate the location of each knife.

QUALITY CONTROL

One of the challenges of book production is ensuring that the correct signatures are loaded into the correct pockets on the binder. Each delivered book must be complete with no redundant signatures.

Printing a collating mark on each signature is a visual method for checking correctly loaded signatures. This is printed on the lap, in a unique location for each signature. As more signatures are loaded, the operator checks the collating marks to see if they match those already in the pocket. If not, the operator loads the correct signatures in proper orientation. The collating marks are trimmed off — the reader is unaware of their use.

A more sophisticated method for ensuring signature accuracy uses barcodes on the bindery line. A unique barcode is printed in a common location for different signatures. As each signature is dropped onto the saddle and the book proceeds down the chain, a barcode reader scans the signature and checks for accuracy. This advanced method is used

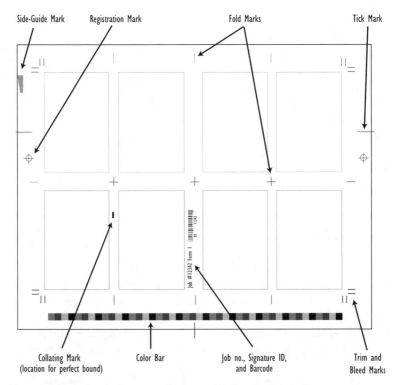

Figure 6-4. Marks are used to ensure quality control throughout production.

frequently in magazine and catalog publishing, and is gaining in popularity in commercial postpress. Visual and automated signature identification can be used in tandem to minimize production downtime.

Quality saddle-stitching is preceded by quality folding. The success of crossovers and folio alignment rely on folding accuracy. It is best for a bound book to have seamless crossovers. Photographs should have consistent color across a spread and the seam should look natural. All folios should be in the same relative position on the page. When you fan through the book quickly, the page number positions should be relatively consistent and not jump around. The page margins should remain steady as well. The best stitching in the world cannot overcome poor folding.

BIND-INS, BLOW-INS, AND RIDE-ALONGS

Publishers often specify an envelope or reply card to be bound into magazines. Four options are available for including inserts in a book or magazine. First, they may be bound in with the signatures, a common practice that requires the insert to be folded. The insert is treated just like any other signature and is fed from a pocket. Care is needed in preparing these pieces to ensure that they can be used from a pocket. Hand feeding is possible, but costly.

Insert pieces do not need equal sections relative to the fold; a minimum of 2 in. is required on the shortest section (called a *hanger*). The hanger functions to balance the reply card on the saddle and secure the piece by the wire.

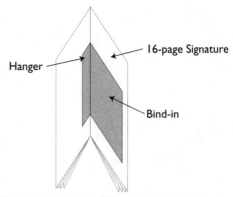

Figure 6-5. For an insert to be bound into a saddle-stitched book, a hanger must be added to the insert layout.

A second option is *tipping* the card onto another signature, which is the process of applying a thin bead of hot-melt glue and securing the card to a signature. Tipping is performed off-line. A card can only be tipped to the outside of a signature; if that card corresponds with an advertisement, the ad must also be on the outside of the signature. Once the card has been tipped, the signature is fed from the bindery pocket just like any other signature.

A tipped card is easily removed by peeling it from the page. This process does not require an additional hanger section, so cards and other flat products already in stock can be tipped in this manner. Tipping is not limited to paper products; it is commonly used to add CD-ROMS, promotional pieces, stuffed envelopes, and numerous other items to a saddle-stitched book.

The third option for adding extra pieces is to simply blow a card into the book. This technique is commonly used in the magazine world — as you see when subscription cards fall out of the magazine. The U.S. Postal Service limits blow-in cards to subscription service only; but if the product is not being mailed, blow-in cards can be used for anything. These are inserted between signatures during the stitching process.

Finally, some books are poly-wrapped before delivery. In these situations, additional materials can be inserted into the poly-wrapping. Any additional material placed in the poly-wrap is called a *ride-along*; these often include subscription information and other promotional pieces. The U.S. Postal Service has guidelines related to ride-along material, so consult with your mailing professional for additional information.

OTHER CHALLENGES

When folding saddle-stitched book signatures, it is common to perforate the head and fore edge of the signature to allow air to escape. With 16-page right-angle signatures or larger, the pages tend to fan out slightly opposite the closed head or foot. Perforating minimizes this creep effect. It is important, however, that the folder operator continually monitor crossovers throughout the folding production run.

In circumstances where stitched books have covers with pocket or gate folds, the covers cannot be three-knife trimmed without damaging them. These books are usually bound with a single stitch and trimmed. The book blocks are then run through the stitcher a second time, applying the covers and bypassing the trimmer. Depending on the design, this process may require hand applying the signatures on the saddle. If you are planning this type of cover, you should discuss the options with your postpress professional to determine the best way to achieve your goal without substantially raising costs.

DIGITAL BOOK PRODUCTION

Many digital presses include saddle-stitching capabilities, but there are differences between high-volume stitching and digital book production. Digital presses typically work with 4-page signatures — either tabloid or letter size, depending on the final book dimensions. During saddle-stitching, the 4-page signatures are handled flat. The sheets are collated before folding. A wire stitch is inserted through the collated stack, and the whole book is folded in half. These books may or may not be trimmed after stitching.

SADDLE-STITCH BOOK DESIGN

When preparing artwork for saddle-stitching, you must consider a number of factors. Since no paper is lost or trimmed at the spine, you don't need to provide extra paper for the gutter of your book, regardless of whether you have white space or a crossover. The book is trimmed approximately 0.125 in. on all other sides. The prepress technician will allocate extra paper for this in the press layout. If any pages bleed, you should extend all bleed elements into the pasteboard by at least 0.125 in.

SIZE AND ORIENTATION

As the designer, you choose the size and orientation of your saddle-stitched book. If the book will be bound one-up, possible sizes range from 4 × 6 in. to 12 × 18 in.; smaller sizes are possible if the books can bind two-up. Oversize stitching is available at some specialty postpress companies.

Common book sizes (such as 5.5 × 8.5 in. and 8.5 × 11 in.) are popular, and fit well on paper stocked at local paper merchants. If you deviate substantially from standard size books, you may be forced to sacrifice paper efficiency in your layout. When getting a price estimate, you should ask your printer if a different size would result in better pricing.

Books are oriented as either portrait or landscape. For portrait orientation, which is more common, the long dimension is bound. Landscape orientation, in which the short dimension is bound, offers a unique look. Impositions for landscape books can include 12-page signatures instead of being limited to 8- or 16-page signatures required for portrait orientation.

CROSSOVERS

We have already discussed the use of crossovers — a popular design option involving large photographs or illustrations spanning a two-page spread. Accurate computer-to-plate (CTP) imaging processes, combined with better folding techniques, have made crossovers easier to produce. From a design standpoint, you want images to look seamless across the gutter. This is easy on the center spread — the middle of the book where the pages are printed side by side — and across the front and back cover; any other place in the book increases production difficulty.

If both halves of a crossover are printed on the same side of the same signature, color consistency is more likely than if the two halves are printed on different signatures. The second-best alternative is to image the halves on opposite sides of the same signature, because the press operator can work to verify color consistency from front to back.

Crossovers often occur across different signatures. If you have a critical crossover, ask your printer which spreads offer the best options for consistency.

When a crossover spans the inside front cover to page one of the book, problems with consistency increase because the cover is usually printed on a different stock than the body. If the cover stock is of a different shade, the image can appear irregular across this spread.

Certain crossover elements can be more difficult to produce than others. Photographs are usually forgiving — perfection is not necessary to look good. Lines and illustrations, however, can be far more challenging. When possible, you should try to avoid situations that increase production difficulty.

CREEP

When signatures are folded, the inside pages stick out further than the outside pages. The bulk of the paper, combined with the forces at the fold, make it impossible to achieve perfectly aligned pages. Generally, a small amount of paper *creep* is acceptable.

When you begin to insert several signatures together, creep becomes a bigger problem.

A *printer's spread* is the two pages that are printed facing each other on the press sheet; this is different than a *reader's spread*, or the two pages that face each other in the final bound publication. Consider a 128-page book, which is comprised of thirty-two 2-page printer's spreads, folded and stitched.

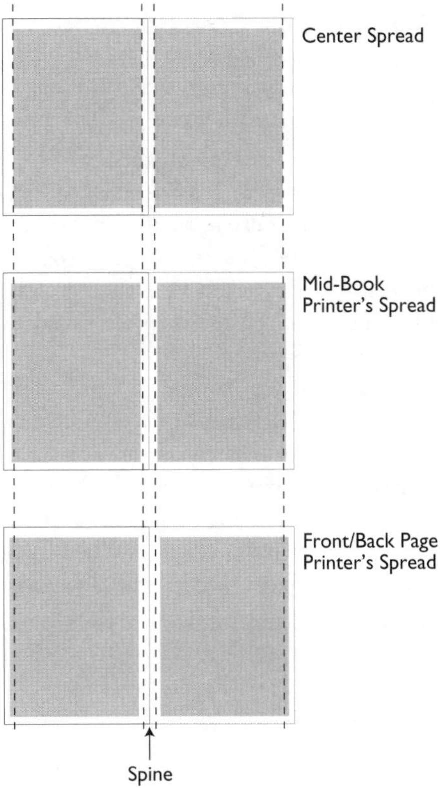

The outside printer's spreads have a much greater

Center Spread

Mid-Book
Printer's Spread

Front/Back Page
Printer's Spread

Spine

Figure 6-6. To compensate for creep, spreads toward the outside of thick saddle-stitched books must be shifted away from the spine.

distance to travel than the inside spreads. The inside printer's spreads have "crept", which needs to be compensated for at the prepress level.

The prepress technician compensates for creep by *shingling* — placing additional space in the gutter — the pages of the outside signatures. In essence, the folios are placed further apart on the outside printer's spreads than the folios on the interior spreads. By adding more gutter space, the folios align properly.

As the designer, you need to allow sufficient margin space to account for shingling. When you produce thick saddle-stitched books, you should allow a little extra white space around your copy.

OTHER DESIGN CONSIDERATIONS

Like crossovers, color consistency across multiple signatures can be a problem. Although presses — and color control — have improved, even the best printers can be challenged by jobs designed with critical color matches across multiple signatures.

An example of a particularly difficult job has a four-color tinted background (for example, 80% magenta, 50% cyan, 15% yellow, and 10% black) on every page of a 64-page book. Any density variation during the press run would result in a slight color variation throughout the book. Obviously, the postpress professional can do nothing to correct this problem.

Because of the manner in which saddle-stitched books are trimmed, bleeds are easily achieved if you remember to include at least a 0.125-in. bleed allowance wherever necessary.

Saddle-stitching is one of the least expensive binding methods, and is efficient for both high- and low-volume applications. Saddle-stitching only gets expensive when production personnel are forced to run the stitcher at a slower speed — usually caused by unusual stocks or signatures that must be hand fed.

CHAPTER 7

PERFECT BINDING

Perfect binding, which glues the book pages to a paperback cover, is a subset of the broad category "adhesive binding". Other types of adhesive binding include notch binding and lay-flat binding. However, most people use the terms adhesive binding and perfect binding interchangeably, and refer to derivations as part of the perfect-binding process. The common theme among all adhesive processes is the use of glue to secure the binding edge.

PERFECT-BOUND PRODUCTS

Perfect binding is used for books that are too thick (up to 2 in.) for saddle-stitching, but relatively thin books are also commonly produced. Perfect-bound books are usually more expensive than saddle-stitched books, but less expensive than case binding.

Perfect binding gives additional strength beyond what wire stitching can provide. The right combination of substrate, adhesive, and technique will produce a book that lasts for years.

The perfect-binding process creates a square spine, providing space to print on the backbone. For shelved books, this is vitally important — a printable spine is a source of information, a retrieval tool, and even point-of-sale advertising in bookstores. For this reason alone, some books are perfect-bound even when they are within the thickness range for saddle-stitching. Saddle-stitched books tend to disappear on a shelf. Interestingly, Xerox recently introduced a square-back saddle-stitching technique to provide printable spines for digital book production.

BOOK THICKNESS

There is no magic number of necessary pages for perfect binding. Book thickness is a function of both page count and the stock caliper. It is possible to have a 32-page book on a heavy stock that works fine, and a 48-page book on thin stock that won't work. A dummy produced on the exact stock will dictate whether perfect binding is an option. Check with your postpress provider to see if the thickness of your book is questionable.

Perfect binding cannot be used on very thin books. The adhesive used for binding does not provide enough strength with low page counts — a certain amount of surface area is required for the glue to provide a strong bond. A bound book must typically be at least 0.0625 in. thick to be perfect-bound. It is difficult to get a square backbone with books thinner than 0.125 in.; spines under 0.25 in. generally cannot have copy on them.

DURABILITY

Consider the products for which perfect binding is used. A typical product is often expected to be durable — used repeatedly, sometimes two or three times per week. Perfect-bound products aren't usually intended to last a decade, but one or more years is reasonable. The average telephone directory might be opened and closed several times per week for about a year. At the end of the year, it is discarded. Many catalogs are also subjected to frequent use during their active period — up to a full year in the case of "big book" catalogs. Perfect binding creates books that can be opened repeatedly without significant binding degradation.

READABILITY

One common complaint about perfect binding is that books don't lie flat. Since the book is glued while it is closed, it always seeks to return to its closed position due to the strength and inflexibility of the adhesive. As readers work through the book, they are constantly working to hold the book flat. To solve this problem, more flexible glues are being developed, which allow books to lie flatter during reading. *Lay-flat binding*, a type of adhesive binding, adopts a case-binding principle — gluing the cover to the side of the book but not to the spine. The loose back allows the spine to flex into a curved shape, freeing the pages to lie flat on the table.

STOCK SELECTION

Perfect binding permits the combining of different stocks in the same publication. For this reason, many annual reports are perfect-bound; glossy photos are bound in the front portion of the book on coated stock, and the financials are bound in the back on text paper. A vellum flysheet may also be bound in the front as a decorative touch.

Traditional perfect-binding glues work well with uncoated stocks, but do not adhere well to coated stocks. However, new glues have been developed that stick well to coated stocks, allowing design flexibility. These glues may be more costly due to different operating requirements.

COVER DESIGN

The front cover of a perfect-bound book is unobstructed; no binding element detracts from the cover graphics. The square, clean, three-dimensional perfect-bound book is considered to be a more prestigious product than a saddle-stitched one.

Covers on perfect-bound books have two parallel 90° folds at the spine. These folds are nearly always scored to achieve a clean bend. The two scores are often produced on the cover feeder, although off-line scoring is possible for challenging substrates. Since they bend only 90° — instead of the 180° needed for a saddle-stitched cover — cracking is less problematic.

Hinged covers, which have two additional scores approximately 0.25 in. outside of the spine scores, are popular. The additional scores serve as hinges when the book is opened. Hinged covers also present an additional place to apply glue. The side glue secures the first and last pages to the cover, adding strength to the book.

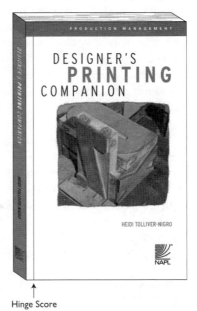

Figure 7-1. A hinged cover is scored near the spine.

Hinge Score

PERFECT-BINDING WORKFLOW

Perfect-bound books are usually produced with 8-, 16-, or 32-page signatures, loaded into separate binder pockets. To collate the book, one signature is dropped onto a conveyor; the conveyer moves to the next pocket, another signature is added, and so on until all signatures have been gathered.

Like saddle-stitchers, most perfect binders are equipped as collator/binder/trimmers. However, perfect-binding equipment is much larger than saddle-stitching equipment. Perfect-bound books are thicker than saddle-stitched books, requiring more pockets. Some perfect-binding equipment may have twenty-four or more pockets — each feeding individual signatures — adding length to the binding line.

Perfect binders also need sufficient time for the adhesive to cure before trimming. These binders apply the glue and a cover, and then nip the cover for a drying period before the book enters the trimming section.

Perfect Binding versus Saddle-Stitching

Collating on the perfect binder is simpler than for saddle-stitching. The saddle-stitcher must open each signature to the middle to lay it on the chain over the previous signature. This is necessary to get the wire stitch from the outside to the center of the book without missing any sheets.

On a perfect binder, the first pocket lays the unopened signature on a belt. The belt transports the signature to the next station, where another pocket lays down the second signature. This process continues until all signatures are collated, one atop another.

Because of the difference in the collating process, imposition is drastically different for saddle-stitching than for perfect binding, even if both are created with 16-page signatures on an

> There is an important difference between saddle-stitching and perfect binding. Perfect binders *stack* signatures while saddle-stitchers *insert* signatures into other signatures. The implication is that a perfect-bound signature will have a series of sequential pages imposed on it. A saddle-stitched signature will have half high-numbered pages and half low-numbered pages.

identical press and folded in the same way. As illustrated below, the outermost signature of a 96-page saddle-stitched book will contain page 1 through 8 and pages 89 through 96 — half low-folio pages and half high-

Saddle-Stitch Imposition

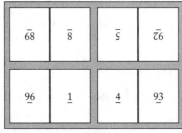
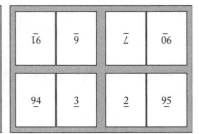

Perfect-Bound Imposition

Figure 7-2. Basic imposition layouts for the first signature of a 96-page saddle-stitched and perfect-bound book.

folio pages. The perfect-bound signature contains pages 1 through 16; it is collated in the front of the book block and contains all low-folio pages.

There are other differences between impositions for saddle-stitching and perfect binding. The saddle-stitched book requires extra paper for a lap, which is not necessary for perfect binding because the signature is never opened. Conversely, perfect binding must incorporate extra paper for grinding at the spine, which is not required for saddle-stitching.

COLLATING, GRINDING, AND GLUING

Perfect binding begins at the pockets, loaded with signatures. Each pocket contains a stack of the same signature. The automated machine places a single signature on the belt, which then moves to the next pocket. If a pocket is missed, or two of the same signatures are inserted, a caliper detector will discard the bad book.

After all signatures are collated, the block goes to the grinding station, where the book block is clamped and rotated on the spine edge for grinding. The backbone is ground with revolving knives that eradicate all folds at the backbone, to separate the sheets. The knives also create a rough surface, for better glue penetration into the exposed paper fiber.

The grind dimension is dictated by the substrate, any applied coatings, the glue used, and the exact nature of the book being produced. Most projects use a grind of 0.125 in. The grind amount is important to designers because you have to add extra white space in your gutter for this grind.

The book block proceeds spine down to the gluing stations, where a rotary applicator spreads *spine glue* on the ground backbone. A blade on the wheel controls the start and stop points of the glue application, preventing excess glue from being squeezed from under the cover.

Side glue and spine glue are usually different compounds because the spine glue needs strength and the side glue needs flexibility. They are not interchangeable.

With a hinged cover, one type of glue is used for the spine and a different type is used for the sides. Two wheels run along the sides of the spine applying glue to the edges of the book block. This is called the *side glue*. Like the spine glue, the side glue is applied with a very slight unglued margin at the top and bottom of the book to prevent glue squeeze-out.

Glues

Among the hundreds of different adhesives, the most popular perfect-binding glues are hot-melt, PVA, and PUR. Each can be formulated for various stocks and applications.

Hot-melt glues, Ethylene Vinyl Acetate (EVA) compounds, are the most common. They are applied at around 370°F and bond well with paper. Hot-melt glues are relatively inexpensive; other glues may offer better flexibility and strength but cost considerably more.

Hot-melt glues have a short *open time* — the amount of time before the glue sets. Although this poses an operating challenge, the advantage is quick adhesion. The paper *memory* — the tendency for the substrate to remember a stable flat condition — is less of a problem. After folding, thick papers want to return to a flat state. Hot-melts cool quickly during the nipping process, securing the cover.

As hot-melt glues age, they lose strength. Most perfect-bound products need to last only one or two years, so hot-melt is usually acceptable. Books that are intended to last a lifetime are normally PUR glued or sewn and case bound.

Polyvinyl Acetate (PVA) glue is one alternative to hot-melt. PVA is water-based, cold-emulsion glue that is cured by exposure to oxygen, similar to household wood glue. No heat is required for application, so energy costs are low. However, PVA glue must be used in a closed environment; it cannot be exposed to oxygen until applied to the substrate.

PVA does not cure as rapidly as hot-melt, so it can't be processed as quickly — a big disadvantage. In addition, the required closed system is more costly. These shortcomings limit PVA to applications that can't withstand hot-melt environments, such as heat-sensitive substrates.

Polyurethane Reactive (PUR) adhesive, which cures by absorbing moisture out of the air, is a third alternative. This is one of the few printing operations that works better

> Both PVA and PUR have relatively long open times to set before trimming. These longer open times are helpful for brief stops but delay the total drying time by nearly one full day.

on humid days than dry ones. Up to twenty-four hours is needed for complete drying — clearly a disadvantage compared to hot-melt.

PUR adhesive binding has many benefits. It is particularly helpful on difficult jobs, such as:

- Books with 80+ lb. coated book stocks
- Signatures with ink, varnish, or press-applied coatings that bleed into the grind-off margin (gutter)
- Synthetic stocks, laminated stocks, and mixed weight stocks
- Books that are used in extreme moisture or temperature conditions
- Books that contain cross-grain signatures
- Landscape (oblong) book formats

PUR products lie flatter and require less backbone preparation than traditional perfect binding. The glue is clear and has much greater strength and lifespan than hot-melts. PUR glue is touted to last longer than the paper itself.

PUR's disadvantage is cost. It is considerably more expensive than hot-melts, largely due to formulation costs. This tends to favor hot-melt for many jobs.

COVER APPLICATION, NIPPING, AND TRIMMING

After the glue has been applied, the cover is fed, scored, and wrapped around the book block. The cover is rotary scored to match the spine thickness. If a hinged cover is used, four scores are applied. The two interior (spine) scores are creased the opposite direction of the exterior (hinge) scores. This facilitates easy opening and helps secure the first and last pages to the cover.

After the cover is applied, it is nipped. Pressure is applied with a clamp to force the glue into the fiber and secure the cover. The nipping station applies force upward and on the sides of the spine. Sufficient dwell time is necessary for partial curing. The cover memory requires adequate nipping, during which time the cover is adhered until fully cured.

After the cover is cured, the book proceeds to a three-knife trimmer where the head, foot, and fore edges are trimmed. The books are usually shrink wrapped, placed directly into cartons, or labeled for mailing. Perfect-bound magazines customarily have bind-ins, blow-ins, or ride-on poly-wrapping (discussed in the previous chapter).

NOTCH BINDING

An adhesive-binding method called *notch binding* is an alternative to perfect binding. Notch binding improves book strength by increasing glue penetration into the signatures. Traditional perfect binding relies on rotary knives and roughening devices to increase surface area on the spine; the exposed paper fiber aids glue penetration. There is, however, a limit to how deep the glue can invade the fiber with perfect binding.

Notch binding is a special perforating process used during folding to create large channels across the spine area for glue saturation. During notch binding, the spine is not ground; the deep groves serve the purpose of roughening. Because the signature folds are left partially intact, pages are less likely to fall out with use. Notch binding can be used with different glues. Even with hot-melt, the increase in strength is significant. Notching is particularly important in books where inks or coatings extend into the glue area.

Notch binding has some limitations. For example, the glue buildup tends to create a fatter-than-normal spine. Notch binding also sacrifices some flexibility to achieve its strength.

LAY-FLAT BINDING

Lay-flat binding is a broad term that describes technologies that use adhesives to produce a book that stays open and flat on the desk. Otabind® and Repkover® are two well-known lay-flat binding technologies. To achieve the loose spine, these machines secure the cover on the book-block sides rather than the spine.

Lay-flat binding is processed similar to perfect binding. The signatures are gathered; the spine is ground, roughened, and a PVA or PUR adhesive is applied. Hot-melt is not strong enough to handle the stresses put on the spine as it flexes.

The next steps differ from perfect binding. The adhesive is then covered with a paper or cloth strip for reinforcement and to prevent the backbone from sticking to the cover. Most lay-flat methods adhere the paper or cloth strip to the inside front and back cover of the book. Some processes use a small strip of adhesive — approximately 0.625 in. — for the cover. Others use a wider strip.

Because the spine is not attached to the book block, it does not crease like standard perfect-bound book spines. Despite repeated use, the spine remains attractive for an extended time.

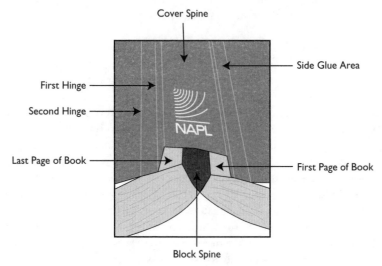

Figure 7-3. The basic concept of lay-flat binding.

Lay-flat binding is sensitive to coated paper and cross-grain signatures. PUR can help in these cases, but be sure to discuss unusual situations with your postpress provider.

It is important to understand how the lay-flat process will impact your design on the first and last pages of the book block. As a rule, you should avoid designing near the gutter on these pages.

QUALITY CONTROL

A number of factors influence perfect-binding quality. Obviously spine preparation and glue penetration are key. Applying sufficient glue without excess squeezing-out is also important. Several quality tests can be performed to monitor binding effectiveness.

The *page-pull test* is a common quality test to determine adhesion of the pages in the book block. A machine measures the number of pounds a page can withstand before tearing or pulling from the book. The page is gripped and carefully pulled with increasing force. Hot-melts regularly withstand two to three pounds of force per linear inch. PUR glues can withstand up to six pounds of force per linear inch. This means that for a six-inch book, a PUR book will withstand thirty-six pounds of force.

The adhesive must be fully cured before the page-pull test is conducted, which makes it difficult to use with PVA and PUR glues. Page-pull testing can be performed during a hot-melt run to monitor quality. It is used more as a validation tool to test PUR books after the fact.

The *flex test* is another way to measure binding effectiveness. A machine simulates a person reading a book, turning the page back and forth. The machine measures the number of turns before the page is released from the binding. Most books can withstand approximately four hundred turns. PUR and lay-flat books will test substantially higher, sometimes up to ten thousand turns or more.

Temperature tests are necessary if books will be used in extreme conditions. Hot-melt and PVA glues are not tolerant of hot and cold weather. PUR books have superior heat and cold resistance, and are therefore not usually subjected to temperature tests. A desert guide, intended for hot, outdoor environments, is an example of a product requiring temperature testing.

One important way to ensure a good-quality book is to pay attention to grain direction. Adhesive binding always yields better results when books are bound with the grain parallel to the spine. This is true of both signatures and covers. The book will lie flatter when opened, and the pages will not warp with humidity changes. Glue penetrates and adheres better with the correct grain direction. Your postpress provider will request the printer run the job with proper grain orientation.

In the previous chapter, we discussed the importance of getting the correct signatures in the right binding pockets. The same is true for perfect binding. During a production run, one must ensure the proper signature is in each pocket. A visual mark is frequently printed on the signature to serve as a queue. Rather than printing on the lap, these *collating marks* are placed on the spine of each signature, where they will be ground off during production.

DESIGNING FOR PERFECT BINDING

Like all binding methods, perfect binding has many design variables that impact the outcome. Poorly prepared artwork will undermine the success of your project. Among the factors to consider are determining size and orientation, preparing crossovers, accounting for grind, determining the spine width, and selecting substrates.

SIZE AND ORIENTATION

Perfect-bound books can be produced in a variety of sizes ranging from 4 × 5 in. to just over 12 × 18 in. Two-up books can be produced and trimmed to smaller sizes. Perfect-bound books can be produced in both landscape and portrait orientation; in most cases, there is no substantial cost difference between the two.

Book thickness is an important factor in determining the feasibility of perfect binding. As mentioned previously, hot-melt books should generally be no less than 0.0625 in.; PUR and lay-flat books require greater minimum thicknesses, at least 0.25 in.

As with all binding methods, some book sizes provide greater press-sheet utilization. If you have some flexibility on your finished size, you should discuss options with your printer to maximize press-sheet consumption.

COVER ARTWORK

Covers are one of the most important aspects of book design. The perfect-bound cover includes face and back panels, and a spine. If the cover bleeds, be certain to allow at least a 0.125-in. margin on the three trim sides. During production, bindery personnel will pre-trim the cover 0.125 in. oversize on the head and foot to trap excess adhesive.

If your cover has a hinge score, consider how the score will affect your cover design. Most people chose to avoid images over the score, to reduce distraction. The score position depends on the type of adhesive being used. In most cases, hot-melt and PUR bindings place the hinge score 0.25 in.

from the binding edge. Lay-flat hinges are normally 0.5 in. from the spine and often are double-hinged — resulting in six total scores. If you design a color break at one or both spine scores (as you see on the cover of this book), you should work closely with your printer to determine the precise dimensions of your spine. When you plan a book cover, ask your printer for a bulking dummy to determine the actual spine thickness. This dummy is made from the same stock that will be used for the job, and factors in glue buildup.

A dummy is still not 100% accurate. Digitally printed books, especially using toner-based processes, are tricky. Ink and toner adds thickness to the sheets. Printing ink is typically not significant enough to consider, but toner will make a noticeable difference. If you have critical color breaks on your spine, you must account for toner buildup.

Most people choose to center spine type between the two scores, reserving the head portion for the book title and the foot for author and publisher information. When centering type, you should identify the optical center, not perfect center. Optical center is closer to perfect center when using all caps. With upper- and lower-case type, you need to adjust your type position based on the weight and feel of the type. Most book designers choose to orient their spine text with the baseline to the back of the book.

GRIND AND CROSSOVERS

The perfect-binding process of grinding the book-block spine needs to be considered in the layout process. It is easiest if you allocate this space directly in your page-layout application. By adding an extra 0.125 in. to your page width, and then placing guides on the master pages, you can build your artwork accordingly. When possible, keep all image areas away from the grind area.

Crossovers are particularly challenging in perfect-bound books. A number of factors impact crossover accuracy, including the size of the signature, type and weight of stock, and folding accuracy.

First, you must consider the grind, understanding that some paper is removed. A big challenge is that readers open books differently. Some put a great deal of pressure on the backbone, flattening the book and creasing the spine; others are more gentle, and don't expose the book enough to view the actual crossover break.

So how do you know precisely where to place the crossover point? A good guideline is to place your images so they meet about 0.0625 in. from the grind-off margin. (You can overlap images slightly beyond this point as necessary.)

Thicker books are often produced in 32- or 64-page signatures. If difficult crossovers are involved, smaller (8- or 16-page) signatures may improve the final results by improving folding accuracy. Smaller signatures, however, may cost more money because more press runs are involved. Although signature layout is the printer's responsibility, you may want to inquire about the imposition. It is worthwhile discussing specific details about crossovers with your suppliers before proceeding too far into a complicated project.

SUBSTRATES

One of the advantages of perfect binding is the ability to use odd signatures and mixed substrates. Even single sheets can be inserted. However, unusual substrates may hinder binder line speed, or mandate PUR glue.

The ability to bind two-page forms is significant. This allows inclusion of supplied inserts and advertisements. Bind-in cards do not require a hanger. Unique stocks can be used to draw attention or meet specific requirements.

When selecting a cover stock, consider using coated one-side stocks (C1S). *C1S* papers have a clay-coated exterior for good ink hold out and high gloss, with an uncoated backside. C1S covers are excellent for perfect binding because they print fine graphics, yet produce good binding adhesion.

Grain direction has been discussed many times in this book. Its effects on perfect-binding quality cannot be over-emphasized. Grain of all stocks should be parallel to the spine. This means that covers, with extra space allocated for the spine, may require inefficient press layouts to achieve the necessary grain direction.

Perfect binding is an elegant and productive way to produce paperback books that last a long time. Perfect binding is nearly always more costly than saddle-stitching. However, for books needing to last a long time or containing high page counts, its benefits provide exceptional value.

CHAPTER 8

MECHANICAL BINDING METHODS

Mechanical binding is a broad category that encompasses several different binding methods, including ring binding, spiral-wire, spiral plastic coil, double-wire, and comb binding. It involves punching a pattern of holes in the sheets, and inserting a physical device through the holes to secure the sheets. Essentially, a clamp holds the pages. The hole pattern, hole position, and clamp style all impact the usefulness of the binding.

Mechanical binding methods are usually simple, as in the case of three-ring binding. Round holes are punched, the pages are placed over open rings, and the rings are closed. The pages turn easily by slipping over the rings.

A common disadvantage relates to production speed — if the speed is slow, the price is usually high. Mechanical bindings are conducive to short runs and are often the cheapest to produce when only one or a few books are needed. For long runs, automation increases efficiency, although stitching and perfect binding are faster.

Mechanical bindings are very durable and work well for books that are used repeatedly. Workbooks, cookbooks, and manuals frequently use mechanical binding methods such as spiral or Wire-O®, allowing the book to lie flat or even open 360°. This frees the reader's hands to do other things.

Mechanical binding methods use signatures in a similar manner to perfect binding. The signatures are printed, folded, collated, four-knife trimmed, and bound. However, because many short-run books are bound by mechanical means, single sheets may be used instead of signatures. In such cases, the sheets are printed, cut into individual sheet sizes, collated, and then bound.

Each mechanical method varies in its usefulness, and each has unique qualities. For some applications, one or more mechanical bindings are superior to either saddle-stitching or perfect binding. In this chapter, certain processes have been grouped together to compare common characteristics.

SPIRAL-WIRE, SPIRAL PLASTIC COIL, AND DOUBLE-WIRE BINDING

Spiral binding, well known for its use in school notebooks, involves punching a series of round holes along the spine of the book and then looping a continuous spiral wire through the holes. The spiral coil can be wire or plastic. Ends are crimped so the spiral does not unwind.

Double-wire, more commonly referred to as Wire-O, provides a look similar to spiral. A series of holes is punched and wire is fed through the holes producing a looped pattern. The wire goes through a hole and then doubles back through the same hole. The wire is fed through the next hole and doubled back. The appearance is similar to spiral, but double-wire offers a slightly different experience to the reader.

Figure 8-1. Double-wire binding presents a more attractive finished product.

All three of these binding methods are useful for books ranging from 4 × 4 in. to 10 × 16 in., and some suppliers can make plastic coil products up to 12 × 20 in. Spiral- or double-wire-bound products include presentations, reports, computer manuals, cookbooks, calendars, brochures, and reference materials. Spiral-and double-wire binding are particularly useful for books that require hands-free reading.

Spiral- and double-wire books also can fold back 360° on themselves. This is useful for products like notebooks or manuals that are cumbersome to hold open in one hand. In tight quarters, folding a book back may provide benefit.

Spiral- and double-wire books can contain multiple paper types and weights. Unlike saddle-stitching and adhesive binding, heavy papers won't impact nearby lightweight papers. With other binding methods, heavy papers put extra stress on lightweight stocks in close proximity, which causes the binding to fail prematurely.

Spiral- and double-wire bindings handle grain-short stocks better than other methods. Because there is some give-and-take where the wire goes through the holes, dimensional changes from moisture will distort the paper less. However, grain direction may impact the ability to use some automated binding equipment. Discuss potential problems of grain-short stock with your postpress provider if necessary.

SPIRAL-WIRE

Spiral-wire uses uncoated or plastic-coated wire to secure the pages. Spiral-wire binding is widely available and works with most materials — from paper, to plastic, to metallized paperboard. Spiral-wire provides a stiff binding edge. It is stiffer than plastic coil (100% plastic — no wire), though the resultant binding is not as durable as double-wire.

One of the hazards of spiral-wire is the risk of crushing. Once crushed, the wire does not spring back to its original shape and the book is damaged. Both the producer and reader need care in shipping and handling.

Uncoated spiral wire is not affected by heat extremes; plastic coil might melt. For applications requiring heat-resistance, such as cookbooks, you should use uncoated wire.

Spiral wire has crimped ends. Some consider this a detractive feature. If not crimped well, the coil may unravel and leave the book partially bound. Further, the exposed ends can snag on things during use.

It is important to use the correct wire size and pitch ratio for the book. (*Pitch ratio* is the number of holes per linear inch and is discussed in detail later.) Thin books require more holes per inch than thicker books. Spiral-wire books can be produced up to 1.25 in. thick. When working with thick books, larger holes must be punched and a greater margin is required from the spine to the holes.

A 2.5:1 pitch ratio is used for thick books, which means there are 2.5 holes per linear inch along the spine. A 4:1 pitch ratio is used for books from 0.375 to 1 in. thick (this pitch is used for most books). Four holes are punched per linear inch, through which the wire is threaded. A 5:1 ratio is used for books less than 0.375 in. thick.

Spiral wire must correspond to the hole pattern. For manual operations, the wire is purchased pre-shaped; it is merely threaded through the holes. Conversely, automated equipment spirals, cuts, and crimps the wire during manufacturing; wire is purchased in rolls and it is spiraled during the binding process. Even with automated equipment, spiral books cannot be produced as rapidly as saddle-stitched books.

SPIRAL PLASTIC COIL

Some spiral bindings use solid plastic coil instead of wire. Plastic coils have grown in popularity because they are flexible and available in many colors. Plastic coils are nearly crush proof; if bent, they spring back to original shape.

For very short runs, plastic coil is economical. For longer runs, however, plastic cannot be formed as quickly as spiral wire. Like wire, plastic coil is formed either in the factory or during the binding process. Automated plastic-coil equipment heats the plastic thread to spiral it. The process is slower than spiraling wire, so plastic-coil books usually cost more than spiral-wire books.

Plastic coil can produce thicker and larger books than wire — book size can be as large as 12 × 20 in. The weight of a very thick book may deform wire, but plastic coil flexes. It can take the stress of heavy books without being damaged. Plastic coil is commonly used for children's books because the coil is lightweight and can easily hold the thick paperboard stock used in this type of book. The flexible coil can also withstand the abuses rendered by the reader — common in this market.

Plastic coil uses the same pitch ratios as wire. 2.5:1 pitch holes for books up to 2 in. — thicker in size than wire. A 4:1 ratio is used for medium books; and a 5:1 ratio is used for thin books.

One disadvantage of pre-shaped coil is that the coil ends are more difficult to crimp during production. The memory of the plastic makes the coil want to return to its spiral position. These more open ends have a greater tendency than wire to snag.

DOUBLE-WIRE OR WIRE-O®

Double-wire, more commonly called by the trade name Wire-O®, also uses a punched pattern with wire inserted through the holes. However, double-wire differs from spiral in both appearance and function. Instead of threading the wire in a spiraling manner, double-wire inserts a wire into a hole, and then doubles the wire back through the same hole. Among the advantages of double-wire is increased strength from two wire thicknesses.

Double-wire uses different pitch ratios than spiral. A pitch ratio of 2:1 is used to produce books up to 1.25 in. thick, and as large as 12 × 18 in.

A metal hanger, used for mounting on a wall, can be included in the double-wire for calendar use. Hanger insertion can be expensive, because it requires splitting the double wire and hand applying the hanger.

Method	Pitch	Maximum Thickness	Distance to Keep Art from Spine
Spiral Wire	5:1	0.375 in.	0.375 in.
	4:1	1 in.	0.375 in.
	2.5:1	1.25 in.	0.5 in.
Plastic Spiral	5:1	0.5 in.	0.375 in.
	4:1	1.25 in.	0.5 in.
	2.5:1	2 in.	0.625 in.
Double Wire	3:1	0.5625 in.	0.375 in.
	2:1	1.25 in.	0.5 in.

Table C. The standard pitch ratios used for various wire-bound books.

Double-wire is attractive and is considered to have a more polished appearance than spiral. The wire seam is hidden in the back of the book. The reader sees only the wire loops.

Split double-wire binding, which uses double-wire in a manner similar to wire stitching, can be used to create an interesting effect. The double-wire is applied in two sections only — a 1-in. section near the foot of the book and a 1-in. section near the head. This method presents a unique impact for the user, but may be costly to produce depending on the automation involved.

Like spiral wire, the double-wire element does not have memory. When the wire is crushed, the book is damaged and possibly unusable. Care is needed during transit — and by the user — to ensure that the wire remains intact.

DESIGN CONSIDERATIONS

Designing for spiral-wire, plastic-coil, or double-wire is simple. If pages are printed as signatures, the signatures are four-knife trimmed prior to binding. Otherwise, the pages are either produced in single sheets or cut to one-up size and collated. It is also common to run short-run books on digital presses in collated sets. The primary design considerations for spiral- and double-wire binding are:

- Appropriate gutter margins
- Determining the best cover options
- Handling crossovers

Gutter margin is critical with any mechanical binding method. Because the paper is punched and a clamp inserted, copy or images near the gutter may be impacted. Additional white space should be incorporated in the design.

Mechanical binding will impact your gutter margins. You should use larger gutters than outside margins. Even with perfectly centered type, the wire may make pages appear optically uneven. To correct this problem, consider adding an extra 0.25 in. to your gutters to keep copy away from the holes. Refer to Table C to determine the minimum copy-free area for different pitch sizes.

With mechanical binding, you have options for covers. The first, and most common, is to use a cover of the same size as the inside pages — all four sides are flush with the body. In this case, there is no spine on which to print. The same margin considerations apply to the cover to keep the wire or coil out of the printed area. This standard cover is least expensive to produce; it is collated and trimmed with the body pages. Spiral books use standard covers.

Standard Cover

With double-wire, you have two additional options. Because many publishers want a printable spine for displaying on a shelf, two cover options incorporate a printable spine. The *semi-concealed* cover has a wrap-around cover that is threaded on the front and back to partially conceal the wire. This wrap-around cover provides a printable spine. The semi-concealed cover gives a more professional look than the standard spiral or double-wire.

Semi Concealed

The *fully concealed* cover also produces a printable spine. As its name implies, the fully concealed cover has no visible wire or plastic when viewed from the front of the book. The book appears from the front to be perfect-bound — until you open it or change the viewing angle. The cover is secured to the body of the book at the back only; the cover wraps around the

Fully Concealed

Figure 8-2.
Three cover options are available for double-wire books.

spine and onto the front of the book. Semi-concealed and fully concealed books are more costly to produce than standard-cover books.

It is critical to design concealed covers only after receiving a bulking dummy. For both semi-concealed and fully concealed covers, scores are placed strategically. A dummy made with exact stock will help you to plan the copy on the spine as well as any color breaks.

Crossovers in mechanical bindings have less impact than with other binding methods. If crossovers are essential, double-wire is a much better choice than spiral. Prepare the crossover like any other binding method.

Spiral books step-up when opened — the right page is higher than the left page, so crossovers don't align well. Double-wire has no stepping effect, so two-page spreads align better. Of course, like most mechanical bindings, there is still objectionable space visible between the two pages. Further, the holes and wire distract from crossover graphics. Double-wire offers a distinct advantage over spiral, but is not as seamless as other binding methods.

Spiral-wire and double-wire are usually comparable in price for most quantities. Plastic-coil can be more costly depending on the configuration and level of automation. Consulting with your postpress provider can help in achieving greatest efficiencies.

PLASTIC COMB (GBC®) BINDING

Plastic-comb binding is another method of mechanical binding. It is common in office environments but less popular for commercial products. Comb or GBC® binding uses a plastic element that is inserted into rectangular holes. The plastic comb curls on itself, crimping the pages. Invented by the General Binding Corporation, the plastic comb is easy to apply. The holes are punched, the pre-formed comb is opened and inserted into the holes, and the comb is released, retracting back to its original shape.

Comb binding, common in office environments, is used frequently for very short-run projects, such as reports, reference materials, and presentations. The preformed combs can be used for very thick books — up to 1.75 in. is possible depending on the stiffness and size of the comb. The strength of the plastic lends itself to using different types of substrates in the same project. The comb can be reopened for altering content, although not as easily as with ring binding. Crossovers are not subject to the step-up that occurs with spiral books.

One advantage of comb binding is the printable spine. The comb extends around the binding edge and can be printed with ink or foil.

Combs are available in many colors. They are, however, one of the larger, more detracting methods of binding. They can easily distract the reader from the cover graphics, so comb binding is less visually appealing than other mechanical binding strategies.

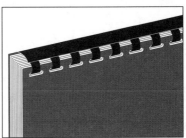

Figure 8-3. Comb bindings are commonly used for very-short-run applications, such as office documents.

Comb binding is not quite as durable as other methods. Although the binding can take some stress without flattening, the combs can break under pressure, particularly with age. Further, combs rely on the memory of the plastic to keep the sheets from dislodging. With rugged use, pages may accidentally pull from the binding. Locking mechanisms are available on comb sizes above 1.25 in.

Because of the comb's shape (flat and square), the pages in the book do not turn as easily as spiral- or double-wire bindings. Sheets can bend and bind up on the comb. For this reason alone, it is not recommend for heavily used books, or books that will be used for an extended time.

Comb binding is comparable in price to either spiral- or double-wire binding, particularly for thinner books. As thickness increases, the comb costs increase beyond wire and plastic coil.

OTHER MECHANICAL BINDING METHODS

Other mechanical binding methods are also available. Ring binding is one of the more common options. Ring binding usually involves multiple suppliers. A vinyl binding company produces the binders and a commercial or stationery printer will produce the inserts and three-hole drill them. They are two very distinct operations requiring different skills. The ring binders are frequently screen printed or digitally produced.

Velo® binding is another common office binding method for making reports and presentations. Velo offers an attractive appearance for reports or presentations. Only a single plastic strip is visible on the binding edge. The biggest drawback to Velo binding is that resulting book does not lie flat. This method is primarily suitable for very short-run production.

CHAPTER 9

CASE BINDING

Case binding is the industry term for hardback book production. When something is case-bound, it simply means that the book signatures have been secured together and bound in a hard cover. Casing-in only defines the exterior of the book — several methods may be used to bind the inside pages. Adhesive binding and thread sewing are commonplace; even side-stitching may be used.

Case binding is an elegant binding method that sends a message of prestige to the reader. Consider a mass-market book. It is frequently published first in a hardcover volume. Later, the book is released as a paperback book. Is this practice simply a way to make more money for the publisher?

Yes and no. The case-bound book portrays a greater sense of worth to some readers. Hardback volumes appeal to a particular audience. Of course, many value-minded readers will wait for the paperback book. However, nearly all buyers agree that hardcover books depict a level of elegance and substance. They are offered at a premium price because of the qualities they provide compared to paperback volumes.

Case binding is the most expensive of the binding operations because of the multiple production steps, as well as the cost of materials used in production This method is reserved for the most demanding book applications. Most books don't need to last for decades or bear repeated use — so they don't justify the expense of case binding.

Case binding is more than a manufacturing method. In fact, bookbinding artists devote their lives to making the book a masterpiece. Professionals in the book arts see binding as more than a method to protect the book block. It creates an aesthetic environment for reading. In rare, limited-edition bookwork, the bookbinder may use special techniques to add touches of elegance to the book.

Edge-treatments such as gilding or marbling can turn the edge of a book into a work of art. *Gilding* is the process of adding tiny gold flakes to the edge of book; *marbling* uses a dye or stain to produce a marbled look on the book edge. Edge treatments are applied to the fore-, head, and foot edge of books. Examples of edge treatments include staining, speckling, gilding, and marbling. Each provides an artistic effect to the book.

CASE BINDING APPLICATIONS

Case binding is employed for books that must last a long time, or receive such rigorous use over a short period to justify the expense. This includes reference books, textbooks, coffee-table books, yearbooks, and personal journals.

Your high school yearbook is an excellent example of effective use of case binding. This document must last for fifty or more years. Initially, it receives a great deal of use — it is opened and closed repeatedly for several weeks. It is then shelved and brought out periodically for more viewing. It may make a trip to a reunion, in which case it receives concentrated use for a period of time. The case helps protect the book throughout its life.

Case binding can be made to lie flat. This is important for volumes that are read cover to cover, such as textbooks. The student sits for hours studying from the text; hands-free reading permits note taking or other activities.

Library books are particularly suited for case binding. They are read frequently, transported in backpacks or stacked with other books. They are often dropped or misused in some way before being reshelved.

Case binding is used for books of various thickness and size. The book block is limited only by adhesive or sewing operations. Books generally need to be at least 0.125 in. thick, and can be as thick as 3 in. Reference materials such as dictionaries are often very thick. Books up to 12 × 18 in. can be case-bound. Specialty binders can produce atlases and other reference material in larger formats.

There are three stages in case binding:

1. Making the *book block* (the inside pages)

2. Making the *case* (the cover)

3. *Casing-in* the book block (securing the two together)

As mentioned previously, case binding only refers to the hardcover application. Numerous techniques can be used to make the book block. The two most common techniques are adhesive binding and thread sewing. Adhesive book blocks are made in a manner similar to the techniques described in Chapter 7.

Case-bound books are made using signatures. Since case-bound books frequently have high page counts, it is logical to run 16-, 32-, or 64-page signatures to minimize the number of forms. The press sheet size and quantity dictate the size of the signatures.

With nearly all case binding, the case extends over the edges of the book block. This helps protect the fore, head, and foot edges of the pages. The book block must be trimmed before the casing operation. In most circumstances, the book block is bound, refined, and essentially finished, then the case is secured to the body by gluing the end pages to the sides of the case.

MAKING A CASE-BOUND BOOK

Producing a case-bound book is done in one of two ways — manually with great craftsmanship, or with automated equipment. The majority of case-bound books are produced on high-speed equipment.

MAKING A BOOK BLOCK

The first step in making a case-bound book is to build the book block — the interior text pages, excluding the cover. The two most common methods to make a book block are to use adhesive to bind the signatures, or to sew them with industrial bookbinding thread. The choice largely involves cost versus quality. Sewn book blocks provide greater durability, but cost more than adhesive methods.

With the exception of digital hardcover book production, case-bound books are always made in signature form. The signatures are printed and folded offline and perforated at the head and fore-edge to reduce bulkiness. The binding edge is not perforated unless the book block is ground and bound with glue. Bookbinding machines contain pockets, in which the signatures are placed for collation. Signatures are gathered one atop the other as they proceed down the binding line (similar to perfect-binding technique).

When making an adhesive-bound book block, glue penetration is important because the book is expected to last longer and provide greater durability than standard perfect binding. Notching techniques and PUR glues add strength. With PUR glues, flexibility is also an added benefit. For case binding, the advantages of PUR usually justify the increased cost.

Thread Sewing

Thread sewing produces a very sturdy block and is used for making the highest-quality books. Thread is looped through the signatures to secure the signatures. In most cases, thread sewing is combined with a small amount of adhesive for enhanced strength.

Thread sewing is performed on an industrial sewing machine with binding thread or cord. The sewing pattern affects strength. *Smyth®* sewing, the most commonly used sewing pattern, sews from the spine to the center of the signatures. However, rather than inserting signatures within signatures, the signatures are gathered or collated one atop another.

The sewing pattern works to secure both within and across all signatures. Smyth sewing passes the thread from the spine to the center of each signature. When the thread is tightened, each page is secured to the others within the signature.

Smyth sewing also loops the thread from one signature to the next. The pattern compacts and secures individual signatures and connects one to another. Smyth sewing produces signatures that lie flat.

Like saddle-stitching, Smyth sewing requires signatures to be open for processing, which means each signature needs a lap to facilitate opening. Once the signature is opened, a needle is pierced through the signature. Thread is looped through the signature and back.

A second sewing strategy involves *side sewing* the signatures. This method produces a very strong book, but the book does not lie flat. Whenever a backbone is clamped from the sides, the book will close; when it is secured through the spine, it has a greater tendency to lie flat.

All the signatures are sewn simultaneously with side sewing. This differs from Smyth sewing, where one signature is sewn and bound to the next. Side sewing requires drilling the book block prior to sewing. Side sewing is not as common as Smyth sewing, but it is used in certain markets where a durable binding is desired, such as the elementary and high school book markets.

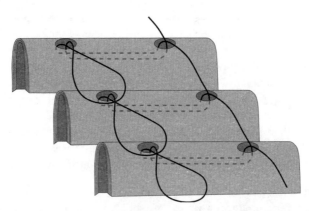

Figure 9-1. Smyth sewing first sews a single signature, then sews that signature to the next in the stack.

A third sewing strategy is *saddle sewing*. Similar to Smyth sewing, saddle sewing involves sewing from spine to center but differs by inserting signatures into each, like the saddle-stitching process. Saddle-sewing is used infrequently and typically works best for thin books.

Comparing Adhesive and Thread Sewing

Cost is a primary factor when considering adhesive versus thread sewing. Adhesive book making is generally cheaper than sewing, but sewing provides a much stronger product. Adhesive binding usually involves grinding the spine for glue penetration; thread sewing leaves the folds intact. When folds are left intact, individual pages are much stronger and rarely fall out of the book. Thread sewing produces a durable book block. In fact, when a sewn book is damaged, it is nearly always because the cover has come off, not from interior pages being lost.

Endpapers

After the book is bound, endpapers are glued on. *Endpaper* is used during the casing operation to secure the cover to the book block. When the cover spine is glued directly to the backbone of the book, the book will not lie flat. This is particularly true with hard, inflexible covers. With case binding, a loose spine allows the backbone to flex.

Endpaper is a four-page section that is tipped onto the first and last pages of a book. Tipping is the process of gluing a signature to another signature with a small strip of adhesive. Endpaper is an uncoated book stock that serves to connect the block to the cover. A thin strip of adhesive is applied to the endpaper, after which it is secured near the gutter of the book block. The opposing page of the endpaper is secured to the case later.

Endpapers are the only means to secure the case to the book block. For this reason, the endpapers must be of sufficient weight and strength, and the glue must be amply applied. When a cover falls off, it is typically at the joint where the endpaper is tipped to the signatures. Either the glue fails, the endpaper rips, or a combination of the two. Problems can occur with unusual endpapers; coated stocks are generally not recommended for this application.

Block Compression

After the book block is bound and endpapers applied, the block is smashed and nipped. Folds, glue, and thread all contribute to extra bulk at the backbone. Rather than have a book that tapers from backbone to fore-edge, pressure is applied to flatten the book (called *nipping*).

Two jaws compress the backbone under extreme pressure. A light paper strip is glued to the backbone to help secure the signatures from the back.

This strip can be a loose mesh, finely woven fabric, or paper material. The book is then renipped.

Nipping compresses the backbone. However, it is helpful to compress the entire book, removing extraneous air. This process is known as *smashing* and involves applying extreme pressure on the entire book block.

Trimming

After the book is compressed, it is three-knife trimmed. Note that trimming is always performed before the cover is applied. Case binding uses the case to protect the book, so the cover extends beyond the body pages approximately 0.25 in. The book block is trimmed in advance to remove closed heads, feet, or fore edges.

Preparing the Backbone

There are three styles of case backbones: flat, round, and tight. *Flatback* books are most common. These backbones are square and are used on the majority of commercial books.

Roundback books offer an elegant look and are used on premium books. The backbone has a convex shape and the fore-edge is concave. When using a round backbone, preparation is needed for the book block. Smyth sewing is the only technique that can be used to create a rounded spine. The folded portion of the signature must be flared using a process called *backing*, which helps to form the backbone to the shape of the cover.

Tightback books can be used for adhesive or thread sewn applications. They are called tight because the spine of the cover is glued directly to the backbone of the book block. This results in a book that does not lie flat, but it produces a stronger binding. The process is usually more expensive but it is used in markets where book strength is paramount, such as the college book market.

The last step before the case is applied is to insert *head* and *tail bands* at the top and bottom of the spine. An enduring book art technique, these decorative strips are made of colorful cotton or silk. They add an elegant flavor to the book, but don't serve any functional purpose.

CASE MAKING

Making the case or cover of a book is an offline, stand-alone production process. *Covers sell books*; cover design and production are critical for book success. The cover graphics are usually preprinted and laminated or coated before they are secured to bookbinder's board. Printing options include lithography, screen printing, digital printing, or foil stamping. Alternate substrates include cloth or leather.

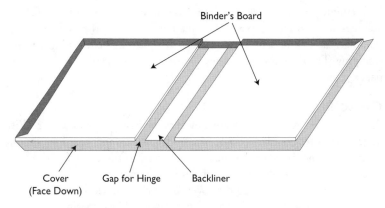

Binder's Board

Cover
(Face Down)   Gap for Hinge   Backliner

Figure 9-2. The basic process of case making.

Once the graphics have been printed, the cover substrate is ready to be tucked onto the binder's board or a cheaper board material. The front and back covers use *binder's board* or an equivalent stiff chipboard. The spine uses a *backliner* that is much thinner and more flexible than binder's board. Small gaps are left between the pieces for book hinges.

The assembly process involves applying adhesive to the backside of the cover stock. It is laid flat on a belt where the two pieces of binder's board and the backlining are accurately positioned. Pressure is applied as the cover edges are tucked around the binder's board. Neat corners are essential to reduce unnecessary bulk. The cover overlaps the backside of the board by about 0.625 in. Force is applied to secure the glue.

The case is delivered flat. The chipboard is initially visible on the backside of the cover. Once the endpapers are adhered, no binder's board is exposed.

Case Materials

Casings can drastically influence the appearance of a book. Some cases are covered with coated or laminated paper. This paper is printed on a lithographic press and may contain rich images. Other cases are cloth covered and quite plain. Cloth covers wear well and offer a durable alternative to paper. In many cases, these covers have a dust jacket, which serves as an additional layer of protection for the book as well as a panel for graphics. The coated or laminated jacket is applied by inserting the flaps into the front and back cover.

Premium cases are wrapped in leather. Bibles and some reference volumes are leather wrapped. The leather is one of the strongest case materials used and can be decorated by printing, embossing, or foil stamping. The thin layer of leather is cased in the same manner as cloth or paper.

CASING-IN

After the cases are made, they are moved to the casing-in equipment. With large automated binders, book blocks are made and cased-in in one succession. The cases are pre-made and placed in the cover feeder of the casing-in line, so no delays occur during production.

Casing-in involves gluing the cover to the book block. Earlier the four-page endpapers were tipped onto the book block. The opposing side of the endpaper is now glued to the case. A thick layer of glue is applied to the front and back endpapers as the cover is wrapped around the block. Pressure is applied and the cover is secured. The endpapers cover the exposed chipboard on the inside of the case.

After the cover is secured, the hinges are formed. This process is called *building-in*. Straight heated irons are smashed several times against the joint, forming an indentation. The flat irons heat the substrate as the hinges are formed.

After the hinges are formed, a dust jacket may be applied. The book is finished by shrink-wrapping or carton packing. Books are counter-

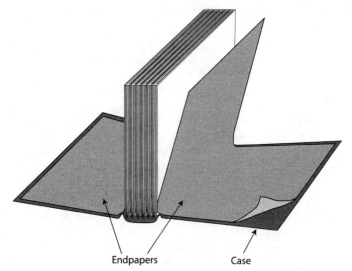

Endpapers   Case

Figure 9-3. Endpapers are secured to the first and last pages of the book block, then adhered to the case to create the finished book.

stacked, alternating and offsetting each book to compensate for spine thickness. Transit marking can be problematic, so slip sheets may be placed between books during packaging.

HARDCOVER BOOK DESIGN

Designing for case binding requires great attention to detail. Because there are more steps than other binding methods, there is greater potential for error. Further, many designers seldom work with case-bound books, leading to errors caused by inexperience.

The primary planning steps focus on specifying the variation of case binding desired, selecting the best materials to use, creating a dummy, designing the cover, and handling crossovers.

You must begin by deciding which of the many variations of case binding will be used. How will the book block be made? If it is to be adhesive bound, you need to allocate space at the gutter for a grind. If it will be side sewn, additional gutter space is needed for the tight binding. Smyth sewing requires no additional gutter space.

Smyth and saddle sewing require a lap, which will be added by the prepress technician during imposition. The lap will allow the signatures to be opened during the sewing process.

What style of backbone will be used? This decision may not influence the layout of the pages, but it will certainly impact the book appearance and functionality. Tight spines will not lie flat. Round spines will increase the cost of production.

Communicating early with your postpress provider is paramount for case binding. You should ask for samples of similar project to get an idea of the look and feel of the book. It is helpful to measure margins to develop a sense of space usage.

Substrate coatings don't have a great impact on sewn book quality, but they can drastically influence book thickness. Discuss with your postpress provider how your binding choice might impact book thickness. Request a bulking dummy. It is possible that sewn books will bulk differently than adhesive books — even with the same stocks. For adhesive-bound jobs, it is best to avoid inks and coatings near the grind area.

Crossovers are handled differently for adhesive books than for sewn books. See Chapter 7 for adhesive binding guidelines. Crossovers are much simpler in sewn books than in adhesive books. Because no grind is used, crossover images typically need no overlap. Both square and round covers lie flat, so the crossover seam is fully displayed.

One of the biggest challenges for case binding is cover design. Unless you have a clear understanding of your spine width, it is difficult to produce tight color breaks at the spine. The hinge will extend approximately 0.375 – 0.5 in. into the face of the book, so avoid copy or graphic images close to the spine.

You should strongly consider coating or lamination for covers. Cover bleeds should be larger than 0.125 in. because printed covers wrap around the binder's board. You should use 0.5 in. bleed margins for case binding, which will extend the bleed to the endpapers inside your cover.

CHAPTER 10

FOIL STAMPING

Foil stamping, embossing, and foil embossing — collectively referred to as *finishing* processes — are often addressed together because they have several common characteristics. All three processes involve a die, and they all require force to create the image. Each technique is unique and requires special skills, but most trade finishers perform all three processes.

Reflective metal is an elegant design element. It is commonly used in label and packaging printing, where shelf-appeal and point-of-sale persuasion are paramount. Wine labels, food packaging, tobacco labels, beverage labels, annual reports, and automobile brochures all make use of reflectivity to achieve the "metallic" look.

Foil stamping is usually more expensive than printing. Fixed costs include the cost of the die and the makeready of the press. Variable costs, including the foil itself, are incurred during the actual press run. Generally, foil stamping is limited in speed, rarely running more than 5,000 sheets per hour. Foil stamping offers high value, but is priced higher than equivalent print applications.

While a *trade bindery* serves printers by providing cutting, folding, and bindery operations, the *trade finisher* is a company specializing in foil stamping and embossing. These companies act as subcontractors to printers in postpress decorative processes.

FOIL STAMPING, METALLIZED PAPER, AND METALLIC INK

Foil stamping involves transferring metal to a substrate to achieve a shiny, reflective pattern. It is most commonly done by creating a die of the image to be transferred, which, when heated, applies foil to the substrate in the desired pattern. Foil stamping can be used for most solid-line and type images. When used in combination with printing or embossing, the effect is dramatic and conveys a sense of richness.

There are optional methods for creating a reflective appearance, such as printing directly on metallized substrates. Paper can be metallized at a mill with a thin application of aluminum covering the paper's entire surface. Metallized substrates are worth exploring to increase visual appeal. Understand, however, that printing on metallized surfaces is different than printing on regular paper, and should be discussed in advance with your printer. The printed result has an overall reflective appearance.

Metallic inks provide another alternative to achieve a reflective appearance. One advantage is that metallic inks can be applied during the printing process, requiring no additional postpress expense. Compared to regular inks, metallics offer a unique appearance. They can be used with halftone images giving photographs a reflective look.

Metallic inks have some disadvantages. These inks contain fine metal particles that function as the pigment. Metallic inks are difficult to print because of the large size of the metal particles. Further, these inks are limited in their reflectance and opacity. They are in no way comparable to a quality foil stamp.

USES OF FOIL STAMPING

Foil stamping requires a die, which has raised portions for image areas and recessed portions for non-image areas. This relief die is mounted in a foil stamping press, where a roll of foil is pressed between the die and the substrate. Only the raised parts of the die actually cause metal transfer.

Foil stamping can be executed several ways. The most common method uses the heated metal die described above. The die can be made flat for flatbed presses, or in rotary form for narrow-web label presses. Flat dies are used extensively for commercial printing, where the products are typically printed on sheetfed presses. In this case, the sheets are usually sent to a foil stamping trade finisher, where the sheets are stamped on specialized equipment. Depending on the run length, the image may be stamped individually, two-up, four-up, or whatever the project dictates. A single multiple-image die can be generated if necessary to accomplish this.

The stock significantly affects the receptivity of the foil. Even with all other variables controlled, some stocks will not accept foil well.

Dies will be discussed in more detail later, but it should be stated now that dies vary considerably in price. Like cutting dies, the cost of many stamping and embossing dies is based on the complexity of the artwork. Since this is a fixed expense, short-run foil stamping can be costly. As the run length increases, the die cost is recovered over a greater number of pieces.

COLD FOIL

Due to the expense of making foil-stamping dies, new technologies have been explored to eliminate this step. A new technique, called *cold foil*, is

---

being used on a limited basis on narrow-web rotary presses. Cold foiling uses a traditional flexographic plate to apply an adhesive to the substrate. One of two adhesives is used. The more popular method uses a *free-radical* adhesive that is ultraviolet (UV) cured after nipping the foil to the substrate. The UV lamp cures the adhesive through the foil, after which the excess material is peeled away from the substrate, leaving the image intact.

The second cold foil method uses a *cationic* adhesive. This method requires a brief curing step prior to nipping the foil. The UV lamps cause the adhesive to become tacky. The foil is nipped to this tacky glue, where enough adhesion is present to hold fast the foil image. After the excess foil is removed, a post cure helps to solidify the image. Cationic cold foil has limited working latitude, so many printers prefer free radical foiling.

Cold foiling is a new process and is currently only used by a handful of narrow-web flexo printers. It is not compatible for sheetfed printing, so the majority of commercial foiling still uses sheetfed hot-foil stamping.

HOT STAMPING EFFECTS

Hot-foil stamping is presently superior in quality to cold applied foil. It is very opaque and can be used to lay a light color on dark stock — white foil on black paper, for example. Holographic foil can be used for security work, or to create an unusual appearance. Clear and tinted foils can also be used for subtle effects, or to simply create a glossy appearance on an uncoated stock. The decorative opportunities are limitless with foil stamping.

APPLYING HOT FOIL

Foil stamping begins with a die. Before the die can be made, many aspects of the piece must be considered. Like all production, each process impacts downstream operations. Planning applies as much to purchasing a die as it does to laying out a press sheet. The die specifications are developed after carefully considering all characteristics of the job.

STAMPING DIES

Foil-stamping dies are made of metals that are hard, engravable, and good conductors of heat. The most commonly used metals for foil stamping are brass, copper, and magnesium. Magnesium dies are frequently called *mag* dies. Each of these metals excels in various ways and has specific applications.

Brass, an alloy made of copper, tin, and lead, is easily engraved and is an excellent heat conductor. It offers a good combination of hardness and malleability. Brass is generally considered the premium material for foil stamping, although it is relatively expensive.

Brass dies are excellent for very long runs, up to two million impressions under optimal conditions. But because copper dies also work very well for foil stamping, brass dies are not typically used for short-run work.

Copper is also an excellent conductor of heat. Maintaining consistent die temperature is always challenging because the cool paper has a tendency to lower die face temperature. Copper is better than brass at heat recovery because it heats and cools very quickly.

Copper dies are not quite as hard as brass dies, and therefore do not last as long. The copper used for foil engravings is actually an alloy, typically made of 99% copper and 1% silver. Copper dies will last up to 500,000 impressions under optimal conditions, so copper foil-stamping dies work very well for the majority of commercial work.

Copper dies can be photoengraved — a distinct price advantage over brass dies, which are mechanically engraved. Foil-stamping dies require a mechanically engraved brass die only when the detail is very intricate.

The third common foil-stamping die is the *magnesium* die. Magnesium is a soft, light metal that is easily photo-engraved. The mag die is inexpensive to make, but does not hold the detail of the other die materials. It is popular for simple stamping projects, particularly for short run lengths. Mag dies will last up to 50,000 impressions if handled well.

Mag dies, as with all foil and embossing dies, must be handled carefully to avoid damaging them. These metals are soft and dent easily. Magnesium dies can be used only for two-dimensional artwork. All foil stamping is

Material	Hardness	Die Life	Cost	Heat Conductivity	Metal Expansion (12 in. @ 250°F)	Die Making Process	Die Configuration
Magnesium	Soft	Short (10,000 – 50,000)	Based on square inches or metal	Fair	0.030 in.	Photoengraved	Flat
Copper	Medium	Medium (100,000 – 500,000)	Based on square inches	Excellent	0.020 in.	Photoengraved	Flat or Curved
Brass	Hard	Medium to Long (500,000 – 2,000,000)	Based on Man hours	Excellent	0.020 in.	Mechanically Engraved	Flat or Curved

Table D. Different die materials have different characteristics, including hardness, die life, cost, conductivity, and expansion.

two-dimensional, but many embossings have multiple levels, requiring brass or copper die production.

The expansion of die metal is a characteristic that impacts die usage. Copper and brass have similar expansion coefficients — slightly more than 1/64 in. per foot at 250°F. Because magnesium is not as dense as copper or brass, it expands at close to twice that rate — more than 1/32 in. per foot at 250°F. Any time a foil stamp registers tightly with something else, or you are foil stamping multiple-up, die expansion must be considered.

Die expansion causes problems because the dies are usually locked up when they are cold; as they heat up, they expand and lose registration. If the temperature is raised even more to increase foil transfer, registration is further impacted. The skilled operator understands expansion, and compensates accordingly. Frequently, digital files or supplied film are scaled slightly to compensate for die expansion on press.

> Some work has been produced using photopolymer materials for light-impression foiling. These materials can be used only on small projects, where the impression is kept to a minimum. When run lengths are short and no fine detail is needed, this may be an inexpensive alternative.

Die Making

Flat stamping dies are made in one of two ways. Magnesium and copper dies are photoengraved. Brass dies are mechanically engraved.

Photoengraving is similar to lithographic platemaking. A photosensitive *resist* is applied to the die surface. The die is exposed through a film negative, hardening the resist in the image area. It is then etched with an acidic bath. Where no hardened resist is present, the acid etches the metal, leaving the area with solidified resist as the relief for stamping. After the acid bath, all the remaining resist is removed. The die surface is finished and it is delivered to the postpress finisher. In many cases, the hot-foil finisher does not actually make stamping and embossing dies, but rather purchases them from an outside source.

The second method for making dies is hand or machine engraving. Brass dies are tooled this way. Depending on the complexity, a machine engraves the brass plate or a skilled craftsman works the metal using hand-carving tools. Greater detail can be achieved through mechanical engraving, though processing time is substantially longer than photoengraved dies. Mechanical engraving is priced based on the hours involved in tooling. Photoengraving is usually priced based on the number of square inches of die surface area.

After the die is made, it is mounted in a press. The press operator controls the temperature of the die where face temperature is most critical.

The die is heated by attaching it to a *toggle* or *bunter plate*, a heating element inserted into the press. These plates heat the die as sensors constantly monitor temperature. A controller responds to the heating probes to regulate die temperature throughout the press run.

FOIL COMPOSITION

Foil is sold in roll form. Numerous colors, patterns, and gloss levels are available, providing various options for designers. Clear, tint, holographic, matte or gloss pigment, and metallic foils of all colors are readily available. Gold and silver are the most common foil colors. There are numerous different gold and silver foils to select from, all varying slightly in shade.

Foil construction varies considerably by application. Common metallic foil has five layers.

1. Foil begins with a thin piece of polyester film, which functions as a carrier sheet for other materials.

2. On this polyester film, a release coat is applied. The release coat is a wax-like substance that, when heated, releases the colorant from the polyester film.

3. The third layer is a color or lacquer coat.

4. The fourth layer is the metallic layer; aluminum is commonly used because it is inexpensive, easy to work with, and stable. Even gold foil uses aluminum with an amber color layer.

5. The fifth layer is an adhesive or size coat, which serves to bond the metal to the substrate when it has released from the polyester film.

During the foil stamping process, the size coat contacts the paper and the die contacts the polyester film. As the release coat is heated, layers three to five are all applied to the substrate. The excess foil — layers one and two, as well as the portions of three through five not transferred to the substrate — is rewound and discarded.

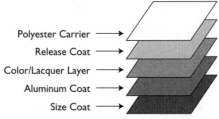

Polyester Carrier ⟶
Release Coat ⟶
Color/Lacquer Layer ⟶
Aluminum Coat ⟶
Size Coat ⟶

Figure 10-1. Metallic foil is made up of five layers.

Pigment foils typically don't have the aluminum coat. The colorant is transferred to the substrate when the release layer is heated. In this case, there is no reflective aluminum enhancing the color coat. The color coat is the key layer for determining the optical properties of the foil stamp. Altering the color coat also creates pattered, pearlescent, and holographic foils.

FOIL RELEASE

The release coat plays a significant role in foil. Of course, it binds the other layers to the polyester backing until heat is applied, but *how* it releases is critical. Foil can be purchased with different types of releases. Loose, medium, and tight releases are all available.

Loose-release foil is used for large solids, where you need the foil to transfer over a large area under minimal pressure. To maximize image quality on large solids, loose-release foils are preferred, because tighter foils result in pinholes. However, loose foils will not produce sharp, crisp edges; the foil tends to "spread" and a slight amount of extra foil will bleed over the edge. The fine serifs of type are blown out and the counters of type fill in.

Medium-release foils are used for jobs that have a combination of both solids and fine line work. Some work is neither fine lines nor big solids, lending it to medium foils. These in-between jobs have enough solid area to warrant a looser release, but still need to some sharpness on edges.

Tight foils don't release as easily and are best suited for fine detail, where the loose foil would easily fill in. Tight foils don't work well for large solids because they require excessive pressure to achieve the coverage needed. Pinholes occur on large areas because the foil "breaks" whenever the pressure changes even a slight amount. Tight-release foils are best for fine type, reverses, thin lines, and any areas of fine detail.

Foil stampers may, when feasible, use both tight and loose foils on the same job. For example, a pocket cover for a new real estate development may have a large solid image of a building with some bold type on the front cover. The cover also contains contact information on the back cover, which is set in fine serif type. Both images are produced with the same color gold foil. In this situation, highest quality is achieved by using a tight-release foil for the back cover and a medium- or loose-release foil for the front cover. This can be done in two runs on a sheetfed machine, or may be producible in one pass with two foil feeders.

It should be noted that foil material deteriorates with age. After several months, a roll of foil will lose its ability to transfer and cover well. The release coat loses its optimum working characteristics and will not perform as expected. Old material should be discarded as soon as its performance deteriorates.

THE FOIL PRESS RUN

The three primary variables that are monitored and controlled throughout a press run are die temperature, pressure, and dwell. Each foil is made for optimum release at a particular temperature. When foil is purchased, the recommended temperature is indicated on the roll. During a press run, the temperature may be increased or decreased to achieve the best running conditions. Die face temperature is the critical factor, not the toggle or bunter temperature, which most temperature probes sense. A *pyrometer* can be used to measure face temperature to get a more accurate reading.

Achieving the optimum temperature for the foil is critical. Most foils release best in temperatures ranging from 210° to 270°F. When insufficient temperature is used, the foil does not release completely, leaving portions of the foil on the polyester backing. By increasing the temperature, complete release is achieved. When excessive temperature is used, the foil might get dull. Other factors can relate to foil dulling (including poor paper surface), but if the foil reflection varies through a run and exhibits a milky appearance, temperature is the likely cause.

Heat recovery is an important characteristic of dies and presses. As cool paper impacts the foil and die, heat is lost and temperature decreases. The press temperature probe reacts and initiates the heating elements. This dynamic process means that a constant temperature is unlikely, so there is an operating range rather than a specific single temperature. The more restricted the temperature variance is, the better the quality and consistency of the foil stamp.

Pressure is the second quality variable impacting foil stamping. Sufficient pressure is required for the substrate to make good contact with the foil. Adhesion is usually improved as pressure is increased. However, fine detail may begin to fill in with excessive impression. A balance is achieved with sufficient pressure for good transfer, while maintaining a clean image. A number of factors influence pressure, including the thickness and hardness of the stock, thickness and hardness of the counter, and the die itself.

The third variable is *dwell*, or the amount of time the die is left in contact with foil. Sufficient dwell is needed to heat the release coat as well as the adhesive layer. Increasing dwell time will usually improve quality, as adhesion improves and images clean up. Clearly, there is an inverse relationship between dwell time and press speed. Dwell is reduced as press speed is increased. Foil stamping is usually easier at slower speeds, where the dwell time is higher. This factor alone limits the running speeds of foil-stamping presses.

A good impression is achieved only when the proper counter is used. A *counter* is a thin board that is placed on the impression platen of the press, serving as a backing for impression. Foil stamping uses a non-relieved or flat counter. Several different materials are available for use as counter boards. Very hard counter boards are good for detailed work where sharp breaks are needed. Other counters are relatively soft and help to even out the impression; these work well with solids and larger areas where too much impression could leave holes.

Achieving even pressure is critical in foil stamping. Without it, one side of the foil will transfer, while the other will be very spotty. If pressure is increased, the spotty side begins to pick up while the other side fills in. Keeping non-image areas open is just as important as getting the entire image to transfer. Even pressure is achieved by ensuring that printing surfaces are flat and parallel. Various methods can be used to check for even surfaces. Presses should be periodically checked and leveled. *Bearers* — metal plates that are placed on the four corners of the platen to help even out pressure — can be used on press to assist with platen leveling.

Although the press may be in optimal condition, dies can have minute surface unevenness. Even with a new die, performing a makeready on the press is a necessary practice. A makeready on a platen letterpress foil press is more involved than on a lithographic press.

The foil *makeready* process includes traditional functions of setting up any press — setting up the feeder, loading paper, mounting the die, and so on. But with foil stamping, makeready also involves micro-adjusting pressures to achieve an even foil transfer. Techniques may include inserting thin tape or paper under or on top of the counter board where the impression is made. By packing or building up the counter, the press operator compensates for any uneven pressure during the run. The makeready process is accomplished gradually. Packing is inserted where a low spot is identified, then on to the next low spot. When the entire image is transferring evenly, the job is ready to run.

Foil stamping tends to work best on smooth stocks with flat surfaces. It is possible to foil stamp on textured stocks, but only if they are compressible and can be "ironed" during the stamping process to create a smooth surface for the foil to lie on. Coated papers generally accept foil very well, as do smooth uncoated stocks. Text stocks can be stamped well in some cases by increasing impression and flattening the textured surface.

When foil stamping on top of printed ink, it is important that the ink can receive the foil. Inks should be formulated as wax-free if coatings or foils will be applied. Most inks are made with Teflon®, silicone, or some other ingredient to make their surface slippery. Slippery surfaces are less likely to be scuffed or marred during transit, but they also make coating and foil stamping over them nearly impossible. The slipperiness of the surface reduces the bonding ability of the foil size coat. Likewise, foil stamping on top of coatings or other foils can be challenging. It is best to coat after stamping if possible (though this can alter the foil's appearance), or to knock the coating out where the foil will be positioned.

During foil stamping, large, solid areas may blister as the heated sheet begins to lose moisture. The foil seals the stock and if steam can't escape, it begins to bubble. Large foil areas should be kept to a minimum. You should provide stock samples to your finisher who can determine moisture content and compatibility (keep in mind that samples may dry out and not accurately reflect the stock at the time of production).

Foil stamping is sometimes used for letterhead. You should discuss this type of downstream use with your postpress provider. Heat generated by laser printers can sometimes impact the base letterhead. Dulling or adhesion problems can occur due to excessive heat and pressure from the printer. The pressure applied during laser printing may impact embossed letterhead.

Press sheets that receive foil stamping should have minimal anti-setoff spray applied during the printing operation. The powder used on sheetfed lithographic presses can wreak havoc on downstream operations. Small amounts of powder are not a problem, but foil adhesion and appearance can be impacted from excessive powder.

Discussing requirements with your printer will help avoid any time-consuming and costly workarounds that try to salvage a job not planned well from the beginning.

DESIGNING FOR FOIL

When designing for foil stamping, it is important to keep several considerations in mind. The more you understand about foil stamping, the better you will prepare artwork that is optimized for the process. If your printer outsources foil stamping (which many do), make it clear that you want a communication channel directly to the foil stamping professional so you can benefit from this individual's expertise. If stamping dies are outsourced, it would be wise to open that channel of communication as well. The more input you can receive from those who actually execute your job, the better you can create reproducible artwork.

Preparing artwork for foil stamping is similar to preparing artwork for printing. In general, you should provide a clean file without any extra information or sloppy elements. Fonts should be converted to outlines. Files should be prepared in a vector illustration application with nested bitmap images, if needed. Files should be saved as EPS and flattened to a single layer. Artwork should be prepared to 100% scale. A hard copy black-and-white proof should be provided with your file, and any elements that register to print, other foils, or emboss should be indicated.

If your art will drive automated engraving equipment, your die supplier may request artwork to be entirely vector art with no bitmap images. These machines use software that reads only the mathematical points of the vector art. Compound paths may be necessary since the machines are not

PostScript-based. Consulting with the die provider early on can assist you in building usable files.

Foil artwork should be comprised of line copy and type only. Tints (grays) and halftones do not reproduce well and should be avoided. All elements should be colored black unless you are using more than one foil color, in which case you may use another color. If you are providing film, be sure that it is produced right-reading with the emulsion up.

Graphics and type have a tendency to look more crowded when foil stamped, so you may choose to use a lighter typeface and add additional tracking or word spacing. Leading may be increased to provide more line spacing. White space that may seem excessive in print will look more natural in foil. Reverse type tends to fill in, even at seemingly large sizes. It is best to use bold fonts for reverses and increase the size as large as possible.

Foil stamping is limited in the fineness of detail that can be produced. Fortunately, most line art is fully capable of being reproduced by the process. Typically, slightly less than 0.5-point is the minimum line thickness that can be held in positive form on smooth stock. A reverse line has greater limitations, typically 0.75-point on good stock. As the substrate gets rougher, these limitations increase.

As described earlier, it is challenging to foil stamp fine, detailed, script type, especially next to big, bold, solid elements. The fine type needs a tight-release foil and minimum impression. The big solids need a loose-release foil and more impression. When stamped together, sacrifices must occur and neither part turns out well. This type of design may need to be separated and run in two different press passes, which, of course, increases your foil-stamping costs. To avoid this, try to use elements of similar size and detail. This practice will help you by running common foils and impressions, and therefore save your clients money.

DIE AND FOIL SELECTION

After viewing the artwork, your die maker may recommend a particular die material (magnesium, copper, or brass). As described earlier, magnesium is common for simple images and short runs. It is the least expensive and is acceptable for many jobs.

Copper dies work well for large-volume work and for artwork that has detail beyond what mag dies can hold. Because it is photoengraved like magnesium, copper is also relatively inexpensive. Copper is an excellent choice for foil stamping since it has many of the qualities of brass without the expense. Both copper and magnesium are easily reproducible, so multiple images can be produced for two-up projects.

A brass die is the most expensive option because it is mechanically engraved. Foil-stamping brass dies are usually produced on a machine engraver, which is faster to produce than hand-tooled dies. Brass may be your best selection when the job has very fine detail, or has a run length above 500,000. Except for the most demanding projects, however, copper can usually do an acceptable job.

When one or more foils are applied in register to each other, you should not trap the two foils as you would with a printed job. Foils do not adhere well to each other, so the finisher will simply take extra care to ensure precise registration. As stated earlier, it is important to report to the die maker and foil stamper any parts of the artwork that register to other elements. The die maker will consider the need and degree of scaling to compensate for die expansion.

You have to specify foil color to your finisher. The actual foil selection is usually left up to the stamping professional. Having a thorough understanding of foil colors, patterns, and releases will help in your design work. A commercial foil guide used to specify foil colors is available from the Foil Stamping and Embossing Association (www.fsea.com). This fan book contains numerous stamped samples and is similar in style to a PANTONE® book for specifying printing inks.

SUBSTRATE SELECTION

You must select the optimum paper stock for foil stamping. Many projects that include foil tend to be high-value works produced in short run lengths. In these situations, paper is not a large portion of a job's cost so skimping on paper quality is unnecessary.

Paper caliper is not typically an issue in foil stamping. As long as a sheet can be fed in the press without incident, thin stocks stamp as well as thick stocks. The biggest factor impacting quality is paper smoothness. If you are planning foil stamping, you should select two or three possible stocks, and discuss those options with your stamping professional. Your postpress provider can provide samples, and run tests if necessary to determine the compatibility of a paper and foil.

You should be careful when using translucent and some opaque foils with colored papers. The underlying stock can influence the foil's appearance. As you select your foil, consider its appearance on the stock to which it will be applied.

In certain situations, highly textured papers can be prepared for foil stamping by "ironing" the sheets prior to stamping them. This is done by running the sheets through the press an extra pass and embossing the textured paper to a flat surface where the foil stamp will occur. The sheets are then stamped in a subsequent pass, resulting in a clean image. These work-around techniques are common to overcoming stamping limitations.

CHAPTER 11

EMBOSSING

Chapter 1 described printing as multi-sensory. Using three-dimensional effects in printing adds interest and stimulates the sense of touch. Textured paper is a common way to grab attention and involve other senses. Minute shadows are seen, as the peaks and valleys of the paper surface influence the appearance of the stock. Paper that is textured at the mill using embossing rolls results in a unique surface that is both seen and felt.

A pattern can also be embossed in the substrate by the trade finisher. You may prefer to use contrast — either a smooth paper with an embossed image, or a textured paper with a smooth debossed image. These dramatic effects draw the eye to a design. The reader feels the image — two senses are involved, creating a memorable experience.

Embossing — in which a die and counter die are produced and the paper is pressed with extreme force between the two — is a technique used to raise or lower portions of the paper in a pattern or shape.

Since foil stamping, embossing, and foil embossing are similar in function and use common suppliers, it would be worthwhile to read the previous chapter on foil stamping before proceeding. Many comparisons are made throughout between foil stamping and embossing.

THE EMBOSS EFFECT

Embossing is a technique of reforming paper in a particular pattern or shape. Many times, embossing compliments a printed image. Other times, embossing is registered to foil stamping, making the foil appear to rise off the page in addition to being reflective. A blind emboss is sometimes created, where the paper alone is formed into a pattern without any corresponding ink, foil, or other colorant.

Blind embossing offers a unique and elegant option for the designer. Blind embossing is subtle but impactful because only depth perception, including the shadows created by reflective light, forms the image. Its

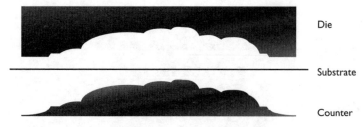

Figure 11-1. An emboss die is the negative image of the embossed area. The substrate is reformed by applying pressure between the die and counter die.

effect is enhanced when a textured stock is used and flattened only in the embossed area.

Two variations are common: *emboss* and *deboss*. Embossing is raising an image; debossing is lowering it, relative to its surrounding area. For single-level work, debossing is always below the paper surface, and embossing is always above the paper surface. The production process is the same for both, although the dies are opposite of each other.

Like foil stamping, embossing requires a die. The paper is forcefully impressed by the die. Unlike foil stamping, which uses a flat counter, embossing requires a relieved counter die. This mirror-image die is used to force the substrate into the embossing die. These are often called female and male dies. Embossing uses a female die and a male counter. Debossing uses a male die and a female counter.

The counter die is made from the embossing die, either during die production or by the press operator after the die is mounted in register on press.

Embossing is commonly used for high-value packaging, business cards, and letterheads, as well as fine commercial products. Most designers want to maximize the depth of their emboss. Several different embossing dimensions and depths are possible, and a number of factors influence maximum impact. Even a shallow embossing depth can produce dramatic results.

EMBOSSING ALTERNATIVES

Before we discuss the technical applications of embossing, it is worth discussing some alternatives to embossing. An inexpensive alternative that does not provide as much impact is thermography. *Thermography* is a technique where a fusing powder is added to a newly lithographed sheet. The sheet is run through a heating tunnel to fuse the powder raising the image slightly where the ink was printed. Any remaining powder in the non-image area is then removed from the sheet.

Thermography is used frequently for business cards. The raised image generates a shiny, smooth appearance. Minute pinholes are frequently visible because the fusing powder does not create a uniform surface. Thermography is easily distinguished from embossing because the front side of the piece is raised, but the back is not recessed. The paper is not reshaped at all, but rather the fused powder expands on the paper surface. Because there is no die, thermography is generally less expensive. However, for most high-quality work it is not a suitable alternative.

Certain printing applications can also create a slight relief effect, mimicking a shallow emboss. For example, screen printing and engraving both lay down a thick film of ink that can easily be detected by touch. Engraving uses significant pressure to transfer the ink so even the paper is slightly deformed during the process. Both screen printing and engraving have useful properties, but are not suitable substitutes for embossing. Neither can produce multi-level nor sculptural relief to the paper like embossing.

EMBOSSING WORKFLOW

Embossing begins with the die. Most die makers make both foil-stamping dies and embossing dies. Like foil stamping, embossing dies are made of magnesium, copper, and brass. Steel dies are available for very long embossing runs. Die selection is based on the detail of the image, run-length, depth of emboss, and cost. Before we speak about the specific characteristics of each type of die, we should address more about embossing in general.

When trying to reform paper, the more extreme the shape, depth, and angle of the die, the more challenging it is to produce without damaging or destroying the paper. For example, you cannot realistically expect paper to start out flat, bend 90°, extend one inch up, bend another 90°, extend three inches to the right, bend another 90°, and then return the original plane. Wood fiber is simply not that extensible. Certain plastics might be able to achieve that shape, but paper will break, tear, or crack somewhere along the way. In this extreme example, the stock would likely rip at several places. Embossing must work with the limitations of the substrate to achieve the maximum paper shaping without damaging it. The die must work with the selected paper and the design elements to achieve optimal impact.

Embossing and debossing depths generally range from about 0.010 in. up to approximately 0.025 in. on a single-level emboss. It may be possible to achieve depths greater than 0.025 in. on certain stocks, or when multi-level or sculptured dies are used. By stepping through various levels, a deeper emboss can be attained. Deep embossing can provide great impact, but can be more difficult to produce because tremendous stress is placed on the paper.

Bevels and Depths

You can realistically expect paper to make shallow, gradual bends. We rarely bend paper 90°, except to fold it. In embossing, we normally limit reshaping to a small taper using a beveled die surface. For example, if we want to emboss a 6-point rule 0.020 in. above the surface of the paper, we use a 60° bevel on the die. This creates a 30° angle for the paper to bend from its original plane. This gradual slope allows more gentle transition to the new plane. A higher bevel angle number means a more gradual transition to the new plane. Common bevels are 30° to 60°, although other bevels may be possible. A 0° bevel is equivalent to a right-angle transition for the paper and is sure to damage the substrate.

Deep embosses require a more gradual transition. Shallow depths can have steeper slopes, but greater depths need more gradual slopes. A 30° bevel is frequently used for shallow embossing — perhaps 0.010 in. or less. When you increase the depth to 0.015 in., a 30° bevel will result in an abrupt transition and may tear the stock. Therefore, this depth requires a minimum of 45° bevel.

Thin objects, like 2-point rules, cannot be embossed as deeply as a thick rule or object. The width of the area to be embossed is directly proportionate to the height achievable. Thin lines cannot be produced as high as thick lines.

Greater bevel angles can always be used to achieve a more gradual transition. However, bevel angle does impact the appearance of the emboss. Greater bevel angles tend to reduce edge sharpness. Depths of 0.020 in. or 0.025 in. need to have at least a 50° bevel in order to achieve the slope needed. The substrate selected will also affect these numbers, so it is important to consult with your embossing professional to determine the optimum bevel for your emboss.

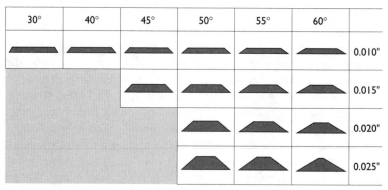

Figure 11-2. Various combinations of bevel angle and depth can be used to create an emboss. The gray area indicates bevel combinations that are not recommended.

SINGLE-LEVEL DIES

Embossing dies are produced in various dimensions or levels. Single-level dies are common for producing line work and type. A single-level die is one that creates a single plane embossed above or debossed below the substrate surface. This single plane contains design elements that represent one "color" only, such as line copy. All elements on this single plane are of equal importance and appear at the same height.

Edge Shapes

With single-level dies, various die edge shapes can be specified. We have already discussed bevels, one of the most commonly used effects. Bevels are used when a flat surface is desired.

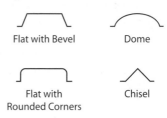

Flat with Bevel   Dome

Flat with Rounded Corners   Chisel

Figure 11-3. Single-level dies can be made with one of four edge shapes.

A second edge shape for single-level dies is the *dome*. A dome edge substitutes the flat surface on the new plane with a rounded surface. The dome shape helps to transition the paper to the new plane, so no bevel is needed. Dome-edge dies are more difficult to produce and are usually hand tooled.

A third edge shape for single-level dies is the V-shape or *chisel* die. This die does not have a flat surface; rather, it comes to a dull, pointed tip. It uses long, beveled edges that meet at a chisel point. It is most effective for thin lines and shapes, but is not used for large solid areas.

A fourth edge shape for single-level dies is the *flat with round corners* die. As its name implies, this die has a flat surface but rounded transitions, which lends it to certain typestyles and line drawings. For example, round corners tend to work well with script type. However, round corners reduce the crispness of the embossed image, so be sure the image is suitable for round corners.

Bevel Placement

When bevels are used, you need to indicate the placement of the bevel. Options include bevel-in, split-bevel, and bevel-out.

Bevel Out   Split Bevel   Bevel In

Figure 11-4. Bevel placement affects the width of the raised plane.

Bevel-in is used when the bevel is incorporated into the thickness of the strokes and letters. In other words, a die containing a 2-point rule has a 1.5-point surface with a 0.25-point bevel on each side. The bevel is incorporated inside the space allocated for the 2-point rule.

When the bevels are placed out *(bevel-out)*, the embossed surface of that same 2-point rule is the full 2 points, and the bevels are in addition to these 2 points. The total emboss thickness ends up roughly 2.5 points.

Split-bevel placement means the bevel is placed half in and half out of the allocated space.

The bevel placement decision is entirely up to the designer. The obvious result is that bevel-in placement makes objects feel a bit thin; bevel-out tends to fatten objects. Registration with printed images can be impacted by this decision.

To review, a single-level die has all embossed components on a single plane above the paper. A deboss has all debossed elements on a single plane below the paper.

Dies can also be produced in two other ways. Multi-level dies and sculptured dies are more elaborate embossing techniques, which increase the dimensional effect of the emboss.

MULTI-LEVEL DIES

A multi-level die has two or more discrete embossed planes. This provides greater dimensionality to the work. Some objects will appear closer than others. However, it does not offer continuous depth. If two levels are used, we can see which object is closer to us because it is on the higher level. However, we don't know the exact relationship of depth, and we aren't certain precisely how other objects relate to it.

Multi-level dies have increased complexity and cost. Multi-level dies may have two, three, four or more levels, each separated by bevels. This stepping effect allows the die to go deeper if needed, since each bevel transitions the paper into greater depth. It is also possible to produce both embossed and debossed combinations in the same multi-level die. For example, a logo may be debossed, and a slogan, company name, and contact information embossed directly beside it.

Single-Level   Multi-Level

Figure 11-5. Multi-level dies reform the paper to more than one plane.

Multi-level dies are excellent tools for separating art into common "colors" or importance levels. For example, the most important elements can be on the highest level with subordinate objects on the second level. The artwork is prepared in a similar manner to a two-color, line-work printing job. Line art and type are used with separation indicated by the designer.

SCULPTURED DIES

Sculptured dies are the most elaborate type of die. A sculptured die is completely analog containing many varying depths and no discrete separation between the planes. In other words, the die maker interprets flat art that creates a masterpiece three-dimensional engraving. Like a statue, the resultant emboss has shape and dimension.

A sculptured die is the ultimate in embossing craftsmanship. A face, bust, building, or any continuous-tone image can be embossed using a sculptured die. Any black-and-white photograph can be turned into a detailed emboss. The die maker converts the tones of the image into varying embossing depths, shapes, and edges. Interpretation is involved to determine perspective. In addition to perspective, the artist must incorporate form into the dimension of the die creating the shapes suggested in the original art.

Figure 11-6. A sculptured die is used to emboss images with the appearance of continuous tone. There are no distinct bevel angles, shapes, or levels.

Since an emboss uses a female die, the die maker works in negative form, engraving the deepest areas as the most prominent components and shallow areas as less prominent. For example, when sculpting a face for an emboss, the nose is engraved the deepest, followed by the cheekbones and eyebrows, lips, and chin. The eyes themselves are recessed from the eyebrows and therefore are not engraved as deeply. This hand- tooled process is tedious and challenging.

Sculptured dies are not typically debossed like single and multi-level dies. If a sculptured die is used to deboss, the die maker would tool a male die building the engraving in positive form. It is possible to have the paper plane split the middle of a sculptured die, having some portions debossed and other portions embossed.

No discrete levels are used in sculptured dies. Their depths are continuously changing at the will of the die maker. Sculptured die makers are artists, just as a sculptor of bronze statues would be — interpreting an original, visualizing, using creative tools, converting ideas through their hands, working in aspect and perspective, all while creating their art in negative form. It is a fascinating but challenging artistic field.

DIE METALS

As mentioned earlier, embossing dies can be magnesium, copper, brass, and occasionally, steel. Steel is the only metal not used for foil-stamping dies because it does not conduct and retain heat like copper or brass and is more expensive to produce. Each of these dies has specific characteristics that will help in deciding which is best for your application.

As in foil stamping, embossing dies are a fixed cost. Mag and copper dies are charged by the square inch, and brass dies are charged based on the number of man-hours needed to produce them. With brass dies, detail and complexity increase costs.

Magnesium

Magnesium dies are the least expensive and are considered a low-end die material. Mag dies are photoengraved, as explained in Chapter 10. Mag dies are used for single-level, short-run embossing applications, where shallow embossing and normal bevel angles are acceptable. The mag die is appropriate for simple jobs. It is inexpensive, but because it is so soft, is only used for short jobs with simple, bold shapes. Very rough stocks, including some recycled papers, can significantly reduce the life of mag dies. These dies do not produce results as crisp as copper or brass dies. The edges of the image appear a little softer too.

Material	Hardness	Die Life	Cost	Heat Conductivity	Metal Expansion (12 in. @ 250°F)	Die Making Process	Die Configuration
Magnesium	Soft	Short (10,000 – 50,000)	Based on square inches or metal	Fair	0.030 in.	Photoengraved	Flat
Copper	Medium	Medium (100,000 – 500,000)	Based on square inches	Excellent	0.020 in.	Photoengraved	Flat or Curved
Brass	Hard	Medium to Long (500,000 – 2,000,000)	Based on Man hours	Excellent	0.020 in.	Mechanically Engraved	Flat or Curved
Steel	Heat Treatable	Long Over 2,000,000	Based on Man hours	Good	0.013 in.	Mechanically Engraved	Flat or Curved

Table E. Different die materials have different characteristics, including hardness, die life, cost, conductivity, and expansion.

Mag dies are probably the most popular because they can be made directly from film using a photo-etching process. Detail usually has no bearing on the cost of the die. For many short-run jobs, where a simple logo or type is embossed into a pocket folder, it is acceptable and provides a cost-effective alternative to more expensive brass dies.

Copper
Copper dies are used for similar applications as mag dies, but generally with better results. Because they are more expensive than mag dies, they are not quite as commonly used. For fine detail like script type, reverses, and fine lines, however, copper will produce sharper results and will hold up longer on press.

Like magnesium, copper is used for single-level embossing only. Run lengths will be up to 500,000, as these dies are not as impacted by rough stocks. Like magnesium, copper is photo-etched so it is relatively inexpensive to produce. Bevel angle is not easily controlled during the photoengraving process, so any intricate or deep engraving is better suited for brass.

Brass

Brass dies are best for any embossing beyond simple single-level production. Because brass dies are mechanically produced, either by machine or hand-tooling, they are well suited for complex situations like dome or chisel edges, or multi-level or sculptured dies. Brass is ideal for any foil stamping or embossing application. It is not always used, however, because of the expense of producing a brass die.

Brass, a hard alloy, produces dies that are very durable, lasting into the millions of impressions. Long-run applications often use brass dies, even for simple, single-level designs because the overall cost and downtime may be less than with multiple magnesium dies. Brass can also be reworked or repaired if the die is slightly damaged. Because brass is harder than copper or magnesium, fine detail — including reverses — can be held well.

When deep embossing is desired, brass gives you the greatest depth. By increasing the bevel angle to 60°, depths up to and exceeding 0.025 in. are possible. These high bevel angles can only be achieved by the mechanical engraving processes used for brass production.

Brass is the only alternative for multi-level and sculptured dies. The photoengraving process cannot determine multi-level dimensionality from film. Therefore, the die artist must engrave these dimensions on separate levels into the brass according to customer specifications on the artwork.

Die sculpting is the biggest challenge for the die maker. Brass is the only material used for sculpted images. The die maker uses hand tools to carefully engrave the brass until the desired result is achieved. Clay can be used to periodically check the engraving by making an impression of the die, making viewing easier.

A die maker will occasionally hand engrave in magnesium, since it is a soft metal. However, mag dies are too soft to be used on press as sculpted dies. The mag dies are used as a master for machine tooling copies in brass. This technique is used when multiple-up press sheets are used, or for other reasons duplicate dies are needed.

Steel

Steel dies can be used for embossing. Steel is a very hard metal and can be heat-treated to increase the run life of the die. Because steel is so hard, it is more difficult to engrave and usually requires an original to be made from another metal like brass. From this original, a CNC router tools the steel die. After heat-treating, the steel die can be used for several million impressions before losing its sharpness.

The Emboss Press Run

After the die is made, it is mounted in a press for embossing. This press must be capable of applying intense pressure to reform the paper. Generally, one ton of pressure per square inch of image area is needed to generate the required force. The size of the press is not only relevant to the physical dimensions of the press sheet, but also the amount of force that is applied during the run. Large presses are extremely heavy and apply several tons of force.

While cold embossing is possible, best results are achieved when heat is applied during the embossing process. Heat helps in reforming the paper fibers. Deeper embosses require greater heat to reshape the fiber. For very deep embossing, the die may need to reach 250°F or more for best results.

The Counter Die

Counter dies are extremely important in the embossing process. The die maker makes the female die, but embossing only works when there is a corresponding relieved male die to entirely reshape the paper. Best quality is achieved when the counter die completely *bottoms out* in the main die. Enough pressure is needed to compress the paper between these two surfaces. The press operator ensures that the paper bottoms out making complete contact with both dies. If the sheet does not bottom out, detail is lost and the emboss will not be crisp.

The operator assures that the substrate bottoms out by adjusting impression on press. *Impression* is the amount of pressure applied between the die and the counter die, and can vary from having space between the dies to having excessive force applied. Generally, the press operator backs the impression off until the image is noticeably degraded. The impression is then brought back up to achieve the optimum image. Over-impressing will break down the die prematurely. Good impression will be noticed by not only seeing a sharp image, but a slight compressing of the paper stock itself. The paper texture may appear different in the image area.

There are several different types of counter dies. A pre-cast counter is one that is made by the die maker to match the embossing die. These are precisely made and provide excellent embossing quality. The matching die pair is pin registered so the two pieces can be easily mounted on press in position. The decision to use a pre-cast counter depends on the volume of presswork, the number of images on press, cost of makeready, complexity of the non-image areas to be relieved on the counter, possibility or re-runs, and pre-cast counter cost. Most commercial trade shops use pre-cast counters.

A second method for preparing counter dies is to use a thermoplastic sheet and mold the counter on press. This is easy to accomplish, particularly with sheet Pragotherm® material. Pragotherm is a thermoplastic that forms to the die when heated. The die is mounted and an equivalent-sized sheet of Pragotherm is applied to the platen. The press is put on impression and closed with heat applied for one or two minutes. With heat, the thermoplastic forms to the die, creating a contoured reflection of it.

Liquid resins can also be used for molding counter dies. Phenolic resin is mixed from a powder and poured on the platen in an area that corresponds to the embossing die. With heat applied, the platen is brought under impression and allowed to sit for one or two minutes. The plastic sets with the heat creating a counter of the die. Liquid resin is not as convenient to work with as sheets.

Molded counters are simple and easy to use, but they are not as hard as a pre-cast counter. Sharpness of detail is less than with a pre-cast counter. Further, press makeready time is increased because the counter must be cast on press.

A third, less commonly used counter is the hand-cut counter. If a press does not have heat, either a pre-cast counter is purchased or the counter must be created by hand. Hand-cut counters are made from layer board. Carbon paper is placed between the mounted die and layer board, and one impression is made transferring the image to the white board. The operator then outlines the image with a knife and peels away the non-image area, layer by layer. This task can be tedious depending on the complexity of the cutting involved. Crisp, sharp edges or deep embosses are nearly impossible with a hand-cut counter. Further, the press makeready time is very long due to the necessary cutting.

Hand cutting is not used widely on a commercial basis. One important exception is when simple shapes such as squares or rectangles are embossed. It is common to hand cut these counters, not only because they are easy shapes to create, but also because of the need to modify them to eliminate puckering on the corners.

PRESS MAKEREADY

The makeready process for embossing is similar to the makeready for foil stamping. Embossing puts tremendous stress in the non-image area of paper, particularly on the corners of squares and rectangles. Deeper embosses present a greater the risk of puckering at the corners. It can be challenging for the press operator to emboss a clean 90° corner for single-level squares and rectangles. Faint creases can develop running away from the corner into the background. Since squares and rectangles usually use hand-cut counters, the operator can correct for this by feathering the corners of the counter.

DESIGN CONSIDERATIONS FOR EMBOSSING

Artwork prepared for embossing is very similar to foil-stamping files. Everything should be created as 100% black, except for any clarifying images, which may be made using gray tones or a spot color. A laser proof should be provided with the file. Any instructions related to registration, bevels, or edge shapes should be indicated. Avoid tiny design elements and fine detail. Reshaping paper requires larger design components.

SINGLE-LEVEL DIE DESIGN

Artwork for single-level dies should be generated in black using only line work and type. Using an illustration program, convert all type and rules to outlines. Bevels and edge treatments should not be included in the artwork, but should be indicated with accompanying instructions. You may provide a digital file for making right-reading, emulsion-up film for photoengraving, or supply film directly to the die maker.

Large display type embosses best. Titles, slogans, and other large elements are popular embossing choices. Small body copy, on the other hand, should be foiled or printed. Small type, fine lines, tiny logos, and extreme detail do not emboss well.

A general rule of thumb for designing an emboss is to avoid serif type below 16 points and sans serif type below 12 points. Debossed type can still be readable around 10 points because of the shadows created. Script type can emboss sufficiently if the thick strokes are at least 3 points, even if the thin strokes are much thinner (because the script is at an angle to overhead lighting). Remember that bevel placement may impact your measurement too, since both bevel-in and split-bevel placements will reduce this measurement. Consult with your finishing provider if you are concerned about your font selection.

Embossed images will appear smaller than the equivalent printed image. Experienced designers often add extra thickness to strokes and stylize their fonts as bold in order to bulk up their designs for embossing.

When preparing line work, realize that very thin rules will not emboss well. Following is a simple exercise to determine the feasibility of the design for embossing:

Print the image as a line drawing. At actual size, all lines should be 1 point wide or greater. This will look like an illustration for a child's coloring book. Be sure it has all the detail you want to emboss. If the images or type begin to run together and become difficult to discern, the embossing will probably produce the same effect. The image should be simplified or enlarged. Very fine lines may be lost, or may cut the stock, during the embossing process.

When designing for embossing, you need to add extra space — tracking, word spacing, and leading — to compensate for the three-dimensional nature of embossing. This third dimension uses additional paper and white space not needed for two-dimensional work. Deeper embosses require a greater amount of white space to be added around design elements. High bevel angles also require slightly more space.

When ordering a single-level die, you may be asked to specify the embossing depth, angle of the bevel, and the bevel placement. Many designers don't feel comfortable making these decisions independently. An alternative is to provide paper samples and describe what feel or appearance you are trying to achieve. This approach is helpful because it uses the expertise of the engraver to provide a die that gets the results you want. If you do provide specifications, all information about depth and bevels — along with pertinent details related to substrate and use — should be supplied with the artwork.

Remember the ramifications of selecting your bevel placement. Bevel-out may cause text characters to run together if too little (or no) extra spacing is allowed. Bevel-in may cause the characters to pinch in thin strokes and serifs, particularly with small type sizes. It is important to consider the placement and size of bevels when designing your graphics.

You may choose to use a single-level die with an alternate edge shape. If you decide to use a dome, chisel, or round-edge die, you will prepare your artwork the same as for beveled work. These edges provide a different look, usually softer in appearance than a beveled design.

MULTI-LEVEL DIE DESIGN

Multi-level dies involve creating artwork with different elements at different embossing depths. Multi-level files need to have all distinct levels readily identified and separated in the artwork. This is usually accomplished by applying different colors to elements of each layer. Separated film is produced for each layer of the die. All the principles that apply to single-level art preparation also apply to multi-level work.

When you decide how many levels to use, you should consider several important factors. Since multi-level images require brass dies, the complexity of the image and number of levels will increase die costs. Two or three levels are normally sufficient for most situations. Many designers like to use two levels, an emboss and a deboss, to create the maximum contrast between the two levels.

SCULPTURED DIE DESIGN

Preparing artwork for sculptured dies is different than for single- or multi-level dies. The artwork is used only as a guide since the die maker must interpret the artwork and engrave the die by hand. Supplying a print is usually acceptable since the engraving artist works with hand tools to build the die.

Because sculptured dies are used to represent shades and tones, a continuous-tone image is acceptable as artwork. Even photographs can be supplied. If line work is used, clarifying tints can be provided to help the engraver interpret prominent, important parts of the design. Shading is also acceptable.

The engraving artist takes the print and begins to work the brass plate, first sketching on the brass and then carving small indentions into it. The artist continues piece by piece, periodically taking impressions on clay. The process may take several hours or days depending on the complexity of the die being produced.

If your emboss registers to foil or print, it is important to indicate these issues when you supply your artwork. If it registers to foil, the foil artwork and embossing artwork can be provided in the same file as two different colors or separate layers. The die maker will consider the metal expansion and ensure that the dies fit.

If registering to print, provide the registered print graphics on a separate layer, which will be hidden before making film. Die makers should know the areas that must fit so they can focus on die size and registration on those spots.

SUBSTRATE SELECTION

Substrate selection is one of the most important aspects of quality embossing. It is important to pick a relatively soft, thick substrate that will reshape easily. There are numerous stocks that emboss well, but thousands that don't. In general, business papers including bond, most coated book and cover stocks, newsprint, index, and vellums do not emboss well. Many text and text cover stocks work fine.

The characteristics that make an embossable stock are long, flexible cellulose fibers. Porous stocks generally deform better without breaking or cracking. Most embossing companies can provide you with a list of recommended papers. If you are using a questionable paper, provide samples before the job is produced so tests can be performed. There is nothing worse than printing on a stock and then finding out it won't emboss.

If the stock is predetermined, a skilled die maker can likely make a usable die for most papers. Shallow dies may work on some stocks that can't handle deep embossing. The press operator must then be able to feed the substrate and then select the best heat and pressure to get suitable results. In most cases, the preselected stock can be used. However, embossing is always more dramatic on stocks that take and hold a deep emboss well.

CHAPTER 12

FOIL EMBOSSING

When foil stamping and embossing are combined, it is called foil embossing. Foil embossing can be done in one press run by using a special combination die called a foil embossing die. In many cases, however, foil embossing is better completed as separate runs.

The embossing quality is nearly always better with two separate passes. The foil is always stamped first, then the emboss is made. The foil must be extensible to handle the stretching of the paper.

Before proceeding, review the material presented in the previous two chapters. Foil embossing requires knowledge in both stamping and embossing. Thoroughly understanding both processes makes it easier to combine them.

WHEN TO USE FOIL EMBOSSING

Foil embossing is a technique of creating a three-dimensional metallic transfer. It is one of the most distinctive effects available in print, incorporating the shimmer of foil with the sensory impact of embossing. Dimension is powerful in drawing attention to your piece; it invites the viewer to touch the piece. By combining foil and embossing, two decorative effects create an interesting synergy.

Packaging, labels, and collateral pieces are examples of products that use foil embossing. Products that rely heavily on point-of-sale promotion, such as liquor, often takes advantage of foil embossing to attract the buyer's attention. The cartons and labels have a regal feel — clearly intended to persuade a buying decision. Because foil embossing gives printed pieces an aura of sophistication, seals used on diplomas and certificates, wine labels, book covers, and business cards are commonly foil embossed.

HOW IS FOIL EMBOSSING DONE?

The primary question about foil embossing is whether to use a combined press run or two individual passes. A single, combined process seems efficient, but it is not always practical. Quality may be sacrificed to achieve a balance between good foil coverage and a deep emboss. Further, a single press run may actually be slower than two separate runs at certain run lengths. The finisher will often recommend two passes — stamping on the first run, and embossing on the second pass.

ONE PASS OR TWO?

Foil embossing in the same press run is possible when a single color foil and the embossed area match completely. Since the foil and the emboss are made from the same die, they must correspond entirely. If they only match 80%, or if two colors of foil are needed, they require individual dies and two separate press runs.

Combining stamping with embossing can be very efficient. Only one die is required; one makeready and press run is used. The *advantages* of foil embossing in a single combination run include:

- Perfect registration between the emboss and the foil
- Less press time for long runs
- Slightly crisper images
- No dulling of the foil

However, even when the foil and emboss match exactly, your postpress provider may recommend separate runs. It is difficult to maximize foil quality and embossing depth in one run. Usually, one or both are sacrificed. In many cases, this is acceptable; in other situations, maximum quality is needed.

The *disadvantages* of foil embossing in a single combination run include:

- Slower makeready time; two runs can be produced faster than one for small quantities
- Shallower emboss
- Slower running speed, which may result in longer press time

Your postpress provider can help determine which alternative is best for your project, considering cost effectiveness and expectations of quality.

The Foil Embossing Die

Like the embossing die, combination dies may be single-level, multi-level, or sculptured. They are used with a pre-cast or prepared counter. However, combination dies and counters have different characteristics than embossing dies.

The main difference between the two dies lies in the outer edges. In order to get a sharp break on the foil, a combination die has a slight cutting edge, followed by a relieved non-image buffer. This outer edge acts as a knife, breaking the foil at the edge. The embossing die does not have this cutting edge or relieved non-image area. Deeper embosses can be achieved with pure embossing dies. The combination die risks cutting the sheet when impressed too deeply in the stock, so embossing depth is limited with combination foil embossing.

You can see in the illustration that the counters also differ between combination and embossing dies. The standard embossing die uses a counter with a recessed non-image area. The combination die's non-image area is not recessed on the counter. The counter must correspond to the die so that only image areas receive the appropriate foil and emboss.

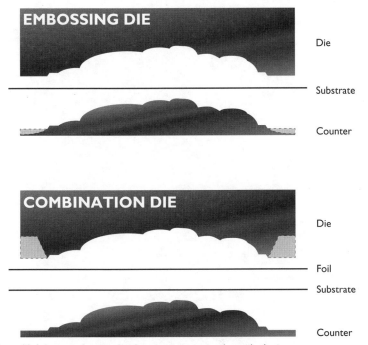

Figure 12-1. In an embossing die, the counter is recessed outside the image area. In a combination die, the die image area is recessed to create a break in the foil.

DESIGNING AN EFFECTIVE FOIL EMBOSS

Talk with your postpress provider to determine the best option for foil embossing. This expert can usually look at your artwork and determine if a combination run is a good choice.

Designing for foil embossing incorporates the lowest common denominator for each individual process. For example, since embossing is more limited on rule thickness, a foil emboss should use rules greater than 2 points. Refer to foil stamping and embossing principles to determine the best practices. When running separate passes, it is possible to make a thin stamped rule and come back with a slightly thicker emboss over the rule.

Since combination runs require the exact same image to be foiled and embossed, you need not create two design elements or separate layers. One image is used to make the single combination die. Design as you would an emboss, and let the die maker handle the rest. Even if separate runs are the best option, only one design is typically needed (unless you choose to over- or undersize the emboss slightly). The foil and emboss will usually match.

CHAPTER 13

DISTRIBUTION AND FULFILLMENT

Getting a product to the right person at the right time is vital to the marketing process. The package is incomplete without a *distribution strategy*, which starts with the decision of how to deliver the product. Your choices include:

- A single shipment to the client
- Shipments to multiple locations
- Using fulfillment strategies
- A comprehensive mail campaign

Proper distribution assures that the pieces will be appropriately packaged to protect them during transit from outside forces and marking. They must arrive in excellent condition. This chapter focuses on post-finishing and binding processes. That's right, *post*-postpress. What happens after books are bound? Where does the flyer go after folding? These questions always point to packaging and distribution.

The method used to package and distribute a piece is determined by factors such as the purpose of the piece; the fragility of the product; the location of the customer or end-user; and urgency.

These considerations lead to the following five topics, each of which will be explored:

1. Transit marking
2. Packaging options
3. Distribution strategies
4. Fulfillment and kitting
5. Mailing

TRANSIT MARKING

Transit marking is an expensive problem that occurs when printing is scuffed, scratched, or marked during transportation. It can be unwanted markings on white paper, or unwanted holes or scratches in the printed ink. Transit marking occurs after ninety-five percent or more of a job's costs have been incurred. If ruined in transit, a job must be reprinted, virtually doubling its cost. For this reason, great care must be taken to prevent marking during movement.

Transit marking can occur when paper rubs against the packaging materials intended for protection. However, most marking is a result of printing rubbing against itself. Papers, inks, dust, and press set-off powder all are abrasive surfaces. If sheets rub against each other, what leaves Los Angeles as a beautiful piece ends up in Des Moines as a scratched-up mess.

Transit marking is most common when transporting books. The weight of the bound sheets adds to the risk of scuffing. Covers with heavy ink coverage are most likely to experience transit markings. For this reason, many printers choose to varnish or coat book covers. Dull varnishes and dull and matte papers have a greater tendency to mark during shipping. Use gloss varnishes with slip agents when possible.

Uneven surfaces — a die cut window for example — can be detrimental in scratching other parts of the piece. If the ink is not completely dry, your odds of marking are increased. Certain ink colors, like reflex blue, are particularly slow drying and should be checked before shipping. Uneven ink coverage, where heavy ink coverage rubs against light coverage, is more likely to be problematic. Preventive steps are necessary for these situations.

The goal is to have no movement during transit, which clearly suggests careful packaging. What are your options? Besides good carton selection, you should explore the following options:

- Coatings or varnishes on press
- Laminating
- Slip-sheeting
- Shrink-wrapping
- Counter-stacking (alternating and offsetting) books

PACKAGING

Packages serve many purposes, including:

- Protection of the product from physical damage caused by external sources and internal transit marking

- Protection from moisture or sunlight

- Help in verifying counts when accurately packed in sets — one of the more important features of packaging

If flyers are wrapped in fifties and then packed one hundred packs per carton, each carton contains five thousand pieces. It is much easier to verify receipt of fifty thousand flyers in ten cartons than when the flyers are haphazardly packed or loosely packed on skids.

SHRINK-WRAPPING

Shrink-wrapping is a popular packaging option that involves sealing a quantity of printed pieces in a heat-sensitive plastic. Flyers or books are wrapped in plastic where three sides are cut — actually melted — and sealed with a hot knife. The shrink package proceeds through a tunnel where hot air causes the plastic material to shrink around the product. Time and temperature dictate the degree of shrinkage. When done well, the package exits the tunnel shrunk in a tight fit. The pieces will not move within the wrap, nor are there any open spots. The product is sealed from air and moisture. Quantities from single books to one hundred or more flyers can be shrink-wrapped.

Shrink-wrapping is one of the best packaging methods for protecting small quantities of product. Although the plastic is not rigid, the overall package is somewhat stiff. Shrink-wrapping also protects the products from dirt, scuffing, and moisture.

Shrink-wrapping has a few disadvantages:

- It is more expensive than simple carton packing or even banding. It usually encloses only small quantities of product. Flyers are usually shrink-wrapped in twenty-fives, fifties, hundreds, or some other small quantity.

- The shrunk package — not durable enough to be loaded directly on trucks — requires cartons, which are easy to stack and handle.

- The plastic must be removed before using the contents. This is less a problem when the packages are distributed to various locations such as retail businesses.

BANDING

Banding, whether paper or rubber, groups pieces to deter movement during transit. Banding is used to secure small bundles that are later carton-packed for shipping.

Banding is as effective as shrink-wrapping for verifying counts. If fifty folded pieces are rubber banded together, it is easy to count groups. Folding equipment can be set to pause every twenty-five or fifty pieces, making it simple to determine when to band.

Banding also helps to prevent pieces from moving during transit. If paper doesn't slide around, it won't scuff. Bands must be sufficiently tight to eliminate movement. Unlike shrink-wrapping, where the plastic protects packets from scuffing against other packets, banded work must be carton packed tightly to minimize movement in the box. Like shrink-wrapping, banding adds cost to the job — though usually less than shrink-wrapping.

CARTONS AND SKID PACKING

Corrugated cartons are the preferred packaging medium for most printed material because they provide excellent protection at reasonable cost. The printer or postpress company, rather than the designer, is responsible for ordering the correct cartons and ensuring that they are effectively used to protect and transport the product.

Safe delivery of the product requires:

1. The correct carton, structurally sound for the weight of the product and accurately sized to minimize product movement. There are hundreds of different carton styles and corrugation media. Each has unique protective qualities.

2. The carton must be packed well. Perfect-bound books should be packed spine to spine, either slip-sheeted or shrink-wrapped. Counter-stacking mechanical-bound books — alternating spine to fore edge — is helpful for keeping binding elements from contacting each other. Slip sheets are added as needed.

3. Cartons must be handled well. They should not be dented or stacked in an unusual manner. This usually involves skid packing the cartons in an orderly manner, staggering the cartons to create an efficient locking pattern. The skid is stretch-wrapped to minimize carton movement. Stretch wrap is an extensible plastic that is wrapped around a pallet. No heat is applied during stretch wrapping.

Skid packing is necessary to allow forklift movement. Skids, also called pallets, are stacked with cartons and wrapped with stretch plastic so cartons won't fall off, making the pallet a single, integrated unit. Forklifts load pallets on trucks for shipping. The skids must be positioned securely to keep any material from shifting during transit.

DISTRIBUTION

Distribution strategies vary considerably. In fact, there may be no distribution strategy at all. *F.O.B.* ("free on board") *printer's dock* means that the job may be picked up at the printer at no cost. This is appropriate for small jobs, where customers can easily fit a few cartons in a small truck, or in situations where the customer wants to contract the shipping.

A common scenario is to *drop ship* the job to a single location. Many printing and postpress companies provide trucking service within a region. The cost is either itemized or included as a service in the price of the job. Trucks are usually loaded with skids by pallet-jack or forklift. At the customer's site, a loading dock may be required. However, in many cases, these trucks have elevated lift gates for loading and unloading.

At other times, several shipping-point destinations are needed. It is important that you discuss shipping in advance with your printer or postpress provider. If multiple destinations are required, exact quantities and locations are necessary to estimate freight.

FULFILLMENT

What happens to the printed pieces when they get to the client? In many cases, they are further divided for distribution to franchisees or distributors. Many printing and postpress companies offer fulfillment services. *Fulfillment* involves taking and filling orders for marketing literature. The marketing materials are printed in advance and warehoused. When franchisees or distributors call an 800 number, they are connected directly to the printer's fulfillment center, where their order is taken. The orders are filled by securing the inventoried materials; any products not warehoused are printed on-demand.

Why do companies choose to outsource fulfillment? Fulfillment can be a very complex process. With small operations, where only one or two different items are ordered, it is manageable. However, when hundreds of items are inventoried and hundreds of franchisees or distributors are ordering products, fulfillment requires advanced systems to track and fill the orders. Using a fulfillment expert can be an important business decision.

Fulfillment frees the customer from these responsibilities. By outsourcing, franchisers and manufacturers rely on the expertise of companies who perform literature fulfillment for several companies. Their systems are in place, including the following components:

- Order taking, including phone and Internet services
- Inventory systems to accurately track products
- Retrieval system to accurately fill orders
- Shipping services, including order tracking
- Payment/invoicing system

KITTING

Kitting is a subset of fulfillment. *Kitting*, the process of building kits of related products, may include more than printed materials. It often involves considerable handwork, as different-sized components must be packed in cartons with appropriate packing materials. For example, a kit may include one hundred brochures, a brochure display rack, a video, two posters, and three vinyl signs. Each kit may be unique, although many times the kits are identical. Customized packing materials are needed to secure each item. These packing materials must be carefully selected based on the kit components to create a snug fit.

CHAPTER 14

MAILING

One way to distribute print is to mail pieces directly to end-users. *Mailing* utilizes the United States Postal Service (USPS) to deliver cards, letters, and packages around the world. Whether direct marketing materials, bills, catalogs, or magazines, mailing is one of the simplest ways to reach those who make buying decisions.

Organized mail delivery has occurred in the U.S. since 1639. The USPS has been under the direct control of the U.S. government for well over 200 years. In 1970, the Postal Reorganization Act phased out most direct funding from the U.S. government. While the USPS can borrow millions from the U.S. Treasury, it is now a private enterprise managed by an eleven-member board of governors. Of course, many differences exist between this organization and other private companies, including exemption from both state and federal taxes and monopoly protection for mail delivery.

The USPS faces huge challenges and a continuing struggle with profitability. Virtually every community and most homes are guaranteed home delivery, regardless of how unprofitable this service may be. But the USPS provides the entire nation's population with mail delivery, handling more than fifty percent of the world's mail annually.

Eighty percent of USPS costs are labor-related. Rising postal rates and increased automation are the primary strategies for the

> UPS, Federal Express, Airborne Express, and similar carriers can also be used for mailing, especially when shipping packages. The cost of using these companies is based on a combination of factors, including the physical dimensions and weight of the package, as well as the original and destination points for the shipment. There are few restrictions on what you can send, as long as you are willing to pay the required fees. This chapter focuses on mailing via the U.S. Postal service, which is used for most direct mail and which has far more restrictions and requirements.

USPS, but strong union contracts hamper labor savings achievable through increased automation. Email campaigns and Internet catalogs have recently changed the landscape of postal use. The Internet has reduced the annual volume of both first class and bulk mail, forcing the Postal Rate Commission (an independent five-member board) to drastically raise rates.

Tensions exist between the business community — desperate to keep postal rates down — and the USPS, needing increased revenue to offset costs and volume reductions. As mailing rates increase, the decision to mail — along with the accuracy of addressing — is more important than ever. Postage can often approach or exceed the cost of paper and printing. For this reason, diligent planning is vital to reduce mailing costs. A carefully planned mailing strategy can save you significant money — particularly on large campaigns.

This chapter provides an overview of mail classifications, methods for saving money in mailings, and techniques for designing mailpieces. It is impossible to cover all mailpiece guidelines and limitations in a volume this size.

Mailing is an extremely complex process. There are companies that specialize in mail preparation. These companies have dedicated software that will use your mailing list to provide the best mailing options. You might want to consider using their services.

Communication is critical in mail preparation. In addition to working with printing and postpress companies, the USPS provides consultants to the design community. Contact your local postmaster to locate your closest Mailpiece Design Analyst.

MAIL GUIDELINES AND CATEGORIES

All domestic mailing guidelines, rates, and limitations are published in the *Domestic Mail Manual* (DMM). The DMM contains the basic standards governing domestic mail services, describing mail classes and conditions

Guides and templates are available through your local postmaster. Helpful USPS tools include:

- Internet resources — http://pe.usps.gov and www.usps.com/businessmail101
- Publication 95 — Mailing Made Easy Quick Service Guide
- Publication 25 — Designing Letter and Reply Mail
- Notice 3A — Letter-size Mail Dimensional Standards Template
- Notice 67 — Automation Template

governing their uses. It also provides standards for rate eligibility and mail preparation. The DMM is the final authority on mailing if discrepancies or vagueness exists in any other source (including this one).

The USPS publishes other helpful guides, including a number of "Quick Service Guides" and templates for designing mailpieces. These guides are valuable for determining methods to reduce postage costs. Further, the templates are useful for checking artwork accuracy. Digital versions are available online.

Most of the content from this chapter was extracted from the DMM and the Mailing Made Easy Quick Service Guide. If you are serious about designing mail, go to your post office and get Publication 25 — Designing Letter and Reply Mail, which has far greater detail than can be published in this book. Further, mailing rates and guidelines change frequently. Consult the DMM or a mailing expert regarding your project.

MACHINABILITY

When letter-size mail is processed on automated equipment, it moves at up to 40,000 pieces per hour through rollers, belts, and conveyors; past an optical scanner; and directed to one of several sorting bins. Machinable mail must be prepared in a specific manner to exacting size limitations. If not

U.S. Postal Service sorting equipment has low tolerance for the method in which mail pieces are prepared. A simple letter-fold piece, for example, requires a single tab to secure an up-facing open edge, but two tabs are required if the open edge faces down. Although this seems to be trivial, the direction of the open edge can result in significant extra expense for a large mail project.

prepared correctly, the piece cannot be processed on the equipment and alternative methods must be used, resulting in a postal surcharge.

It is important to design machinable pieces. If not, your mailing costs will be higher. If a letter, flat, or parcel cannot be sorted through machinery, it may be subject to a nonmachinable surcharge. Non-machinable surcharges apply to letter-size mail in the following situations:

- The *aspect ratio* (length divided by height) is less than 1.3 or more than 2.5. For example, a #10 envelope has an aspect ratio of 2.3 (9.5 in. / 4.125 in. = 2.3)

- The length is more than 11.5 in. or height is more than 6.125 in.

- The piece is thicker than 0.25 in.

- The piece is too rigid, or has items that cause uneven thickness

- The piece is enclosed in polywrap or plastic material

MAILABILITY

Not everything is mailable, at least not without being repackaged. Pieces that are not mailable include:

- Items under 3.5 × 5 in., without inserting into a larger envelope
- Anything less than 0.007 in. thick

In addition to these requirements, all mailpieces less than 0.25 in. thick (except keys and identification devices) must be rectangular (or square) to be mailed. MarketMail, a new standard mail category, permits non-rectangular mail by bypassing most sorting equipment.

CLASSIFICATION

Mail is classified into four categories, each with its own characteristics, qualifications, and rates. These are:

- First-class
- Periodicals
- Standard
- Package services

First-Class Mail

Nearly all stamped mailings are first-class (although bulk mailings may use stamps too). All personal correspondence, bills and statements, and hand-addressed envelopes are sent first-class. Any mailpiece can be sent first-class if desired or required by not meeting volume requirements for other categories.

There are two subclasses of first-class mail:

- Cards and postcards
- Letters, flats, and parcels

Cards are mailed at a cheaper rate than letters, flats, and parcels. To qualify, a *card* must be formed either of one piece of paper or cardstock or of two pieces of paper permanently and uniformly bonded together. They must be between 0.007 – 0.016 in. thick, have uniform thickness, and cannot exceed 4.5 in. height or 6 in. length.

First-class letters and flats are limited to 13 ounces. *Letters* are pieces up to 6.125 × 11.5 in., and up to 0.25 in. thick. The longest dimension is always parallel to the address as read.

Flats are larger than letters, up to 12 in. high, 15 in. long, and 0.75 in. thick. They are called flats because they are processed flat, where letters and cards are sorted on edge. Because flats are charged at a higher rate, you should pay close attention to these dimensions. Mail exceeding dimensions for letters or flats are normally considered parcels, which are sent at a higher rate.

First-class pieces weighing more than 13 ounces are sent as *priority mail*, a first-class category for heavier pieces or expedited delivery service. Any mailing, even pieces that meet weight requirements of other classes, may use priority mail.

Periodicals Mail

Periodicals rates are used for magazines, newspapers, and other publications whose primary purpose is transmitting information to an established list of subscribers or requesters. To qualify, the periodical must be published on a regular schedule, at least four times per year from a known office of publication. Standards for circulation, documentation, advertising limits, and other conditions vary by type of periodical.

Periodicals rates are complex. They usually include a per-piece charge, a per-pound charge (which differs for advertising and non-advertising pages), and applicable discounts. The exact rate may differ from issue to issue, even when the weight stays the same. The ratio of advertising to editorial content affects the mailing price.

All periodicals must apply to be mailed in one of five categories. Records must be maintained by the publisher to support the application and to confirm eligibility for a particular category.

- **General publications.** These must have a minimum fifty percent paid circulation and can contain no more than seventy-five percent advertising in half the issues published during a twelve-month period.

- **Requester publications.** These must have a minimum fifty percent of the circulated copies either requested or paid for by the recipient. Requester publications must also have a minimum of twenty-four pages and advertising may not exceed seventy-five percent in any one issue. Both requester and general publications must keep an accurate list of requesters and subscribers.

- **Institutions and societies publications.** Certain publications qualify for additional discounts. Presence of advertising content, the specific group publishing the piece, the frequency of publication, and the goal of the piece are all considered to determine eligibility for this discount.

- **Foreign publications.** To distribute publications under periodicals mailing privileges, foreign publications must establish an office of publication in the U.S. These publications must not violate any United States copyright, and some advertising restrictions apply.

- **Publications of State Departments of Agriculture.** State Departments of Agriculture may publish one publication that furthers the objectives of the department; these publications may not contain any advertising.

There are also two periodicals subclasses — in-county and outside-county — that are determined by the geographical distribution of a single issue. Outside-county periodicals are more expensive than those qualifying for in-county rates. Because these subclasses are based on actual distribution, a given issue of a publication may include both in-county and outside-county rates.

As discussed previously, magazines may be polywrapped with subscription forms or other advertising materials. These *ride-alongs* have guidelines for their use. Ride-along rates for standard mail matter enclosed with periodicals provide a cost-effective way to send subscription information without a separate mailing.

Standard Mail

Standard mail is used for advertising mail, catalogs, and newsletters of a non-personal nature, not required to be mailed as first-class mail (such as bills and statements). Standard mail must weigh less than 16 ounces, and a minimum volume of 200 pieces or 50 pounds in the same processing category is required. There are four standard mail subclasses: regular, nonprofit, enhanced carrier route, and nonprofit enhanced carrier route.

To receive standard rates, mail must be placed in trays or sacks. Nonprofit rates are available for qualifying organizations.

Enhanced carrier route rates are available for high-saturation areas where ninety percent of the total active residential deliveries are receiving the piece; or for high-density areas, where at least 125 pieces must be prepared for each carrier route. The mail must be sorted in letter-carrier walk sequence.

Enhanced carrier route and nonprofit enhanced carrier route subclasses are designed for markets characterized by flat-size advertising and high-density letter mail. The dense geographical concentration of mail in these subclasses allows pieces to bypass mail-processing operations. Enhanced carrier route rates require high levels of sorting and automation. To qualify for this rate, letter-rate pieces must be 100% delivery-point bar-coded (discussed below) and must be compatible with automation equipment.

A single job may run at several different rates — 120,000 may run at standard enhanced carrier route rates; 100,000 at standard automation rates; 8,000 at standard presort rates; and 800 at first-class rates. As many pieces as possible will run at the cheapest rates.

Package Services
Package services consists of four subclasses: parcel post, bound printed matter (BPM), media mail, and library mail. Of these, BPM — catalogs, directories, books, and other printed material that weigh up to 15 pounds and meets specific eligibility requirements — is most applicable to printing and postpress.

Many thinner catalogs (under 0.25 in.) are mailed using flat size standard mail. The thickest catalogs, like a department store "Big Book" catalog, use BPM rates. Books and directories may also qualify for package services rates.

ANATOMY OF A MAILPIECE

Mail is prepared in a precise way. The size and thickness of the piece, together with the location of each design element, impacts the quality. As stated earlier, there are four common mailpiece sizes:

- **Cards.** These are single or double sheets from 3.5 × 5 in. to 4.25 × 6 in., varying in thickness from 0.007 – 0.016 in. Cards over 4.25 × 6 in. can be mailed at letter-sized rates with a thickness of 0.009 – 0.016 in.

- **Letter-sized.** These are envelopes or flyers from 3.5 × 5 in. to 6.125 × 11.5 in., varying in thickness from 0.007 – 0.25 in.

- **Flats.** These are envelopes, flyers, or bound catalogs that don't fit letter-sized criteria. A piece is a flat if it is longer than 11.5 in., taller than 6.125 in., or thicker than 0.25 in. The maximum dimensions for a flat are 12 × 15 in. and 0.75 in. thick.

- **Parcels.** These include matter longer than 15 in., taller than 12 in., or thicker than 0.75 in. Pieces under 13 ounces travel first class; pieces over 13 ounces either travel priority mail or parcel post.

Remember, for cards and letters to be machinable and processed through postal sorting equipment, they must have an aspect ratio between 1.3 and 2.5. Flats must be rectangular but do not have aspect ratio limitations.

Figure 14-1. shows the design components of business reply mail.

BUSINESS REPLY MAIL
FIRST-CLASS MAIL   PERMIT NO. 1234   MADISON, WI
POSTAGE WILL BE PAID BY ADDRESSEE

MR MALCOLM KEIF
SOME COMPANY INC
300 CALIFORNIA ST
MADISON WI 55127-0000

NO POSTAGE
NECESSARY
IF MAILED
IN THE
UNITED STATES

Figure 14-1. The components of a #10 business reply mail envelope.

1. "No Postage Necessary" endorsement
2. Horizontal bars
   - At least 1 in. long and 1/16 to 3/16 in. thick
   - Bottom bar must be above the top of the address delivery line
3. Facing identification mark (FIM)
   - Top edge must be within 0.125 in. of the envelope's top edge
   - Lines must be 0.5 to 0.75 in. high.
   - Right-most bar 2 in. from envelope's right edge.
4. Business reply legend, permit number, postage endorsement
   - "BUSINESS REPLY MAIL" must be at least 3/16 in. high
   - Type is set in all capitals
5. Complete delivery address
   - At least 0.625 in. from the envelope's bottom edge
   - Not more than 2.25 in. from the envelope's bottom edge
   - At least 0.5 in. from the horizontal bars
6. Barcode and barcode-clear zone.
   - Begin 3.5 to 4.25 in. from the envelope's right edge
   - Must be 0.25 in. from the envelope's bottom edge.
   - The barcode-clear zone is bottom-right corner of the envelope, measuring 0.625 in. high × 4.75 in. wide.

Each of these elements serves a unique purpose and must be meticulously designed and placed. The "No Postage Necessary" endorsement is used to identify an envelope not needing postage. The horizontal bars simply make the endorsement stand out. It clearly identifies the piece as business reply mail.

The facing identification mark (FIM) is a series of five or six vertical bars used by automated postal equipment to identify, orient, and separate reply mail. The FIM requires a clear zone, where no additional marks can appear. The business reply legend, permit number, and postage payment endorsement identify how the postage will be paid. The complete delivery address appears in the correct spot for automated equipment to read it. Finally, the POSTNET barcode is placed with a clear zone around it.

Other elements can also appear in the design. A return address may be placed in the upper left corner, and a service request endorsement may be placed on the mail.

SERVICE REQUESTS

Service requests tell the USPS how you want them to handle pieces that are undeliverable as addressed. These four service requests differ slightly for standard mail and first-class mail:

- **Address service requested.** This returns the piece to the sender together with the reason for non-delivery. For first-class, there is no charge for this service; if a change-of-address is on file, the piece will be forwarded for a period of time. For standard mail, there is a charge for return of the mailpiece or address correction.

- **Return service requested.** Using this request, the piece is returned at no charge with the reason for non-delivery. Standard mailings are charged the first-class mail rate for the returned piece.

- **Change service requested.** This is used by mailers who participate in the electronic Address Change Service (discussed below). If the mailpiece is sent first-class, it is returned to the sender; standard mail is thrown away. An address correction fee is charged for both first-class and standard mail.

- **Forwarding service requested.** This forwards the piece for a period of time when a change-of-address is on file. If undeliverable, the piece is returned with the reason for nondelivery. First-class mailings are not charged for this service. When a person submits a change-of-address, mail is typically forwarded for a period up to twelve months. During the thirteenth through eighteenth months, the mailpiece is returned to the sender at no charge with the new address attached. Standard mailings are charged a weighted fee for returned mailpieces.

ADDRESS QUALITY

One of the most important aspects of preparing mail projects is ensuring address quality. This is a multifaceted topic: The data must be complete and clean. The address should be formatted well. And the address needs to be accurately placed on the mailpiece.

Good address quality ensures smooth processing through automated equipment and maximum postal discounts. It is estimated that mailers lose over two billion dollars annually on incomplete and inaccurate addresses.

Certification

In order to qualify for certain postal discounts, the USPS has minimum quality standards for addresses. The cleaner your list, the cheaper your postal rates. Your mailing supplier should have the tools necessary to certify the accuracy of your database. Nobody will guarantee a particular individual lives in a house, but mailers can ensure an address is deliverable.

A certifying process must be used to ensure the accuracy of 5-digit ZIP codes. Most mailers use *Coding Accuracy Support System (CASS)* — certified address-matching software. These software applications work with USPS Address Information System products to qualify addresses for discounts. The process involves comparing your list to the USPS files.

Sometimes addresses cannot be matched, most commonly because of incomplete data. For example, *pre-directional* (directional data including North, South, East, and West) data may be missing. If two addresses match "100 California Street" in Lee's Summit, MO, then the address must be updated to read:

100 W CALIFORNIA ST

In this example, the "W" is a predirectional. The "ST" is a designator. *Designators* include Street, Road, Place, Court, and others.

Also note that the example address is all capitals. Standardization is also an important part of address quality. Mailing software not only CASS-certifies, but it also standardizes, which includes the following tasks:

- Lowercase is converted to uppercase and punctuation is removed

- Secondary address information, such as apartment number, is standardized

- Delivery address line information, including apartment number, is placed on the same line

- Pre-directionals, like W (west) or E (east), are placed in the delivery address line

- Correct suffix is given for delivery address

- Spelling of street name is corrected

- Spelling of city name is corrected

- Standard state name abbreviation is given

- ZIP code is corrected

- Correct ZIP+4 code is given

To keep your mailing list up-to-date, be diligent in tracking customers and requesting notifications of address changes. Many mailers also use a method to monitor address currency with one or more of the following:

- Address Change Service (ACS)

- National Change of Address (NCOA)

- FASTforward[SM]

ACS participants receive an electronic notice of new address information, significantly reducing the number of hard copy notices received. By using "Change Service Requested", the first-class mailer receives notice and may prevent the forwarding or returning of mail if desired. ACS is available for first-class, periodicals, and standard mail.

NCOA corrects mailing lists using strict Postal Service-approved name- and address-matching logic. This system contains individuals, families, and businesses that have moved within the preceding three years. (Of course, each must file a change-of-address form.) NCOA service is provided by private companies under the license of the USPS. The USPS sends weekly updates to these service providers. NCOA service helps reduce undeliverable-as-addressed mail by correcting addresses before entering the mailstream.

The FASTforward system is a user-licensed computer system containing FASTforward name- and address-matching software, and a change-of-address database. FASTforward for Mailing List Correction provides licensees with an electronic update to computer-based name and address lists. If a name and address match a change-of-address filed within the preceding six months, the mailing list is updated.

Mailers use one of these systems to verify the currency of their addresses. This not only saves money, but is also used to certify a list to receive deep postal discounts.

POSTAL DISCOUNTS

Postal discounts are critical. Without them, mailers would be paying billions more to send their pieces. Because mailings can be large, even $0.004 saved per piece can reap substantial benefits.

Postal discounts generally involve using sorting strategies, applying barcodes for automation, mixing various mail campaigns together to increase volumes, and using multiple destination entry points.

PRESORTING

Presorting involves sequencing all pieces of a mailing in ZIP code or delivery-point order. By presorting, mailpieces can bypass some of the USPS sorting equipment and qualify for postage discounts.

The USPS offers a better discount for nonprofit mailings. Presorted regular and nonprofit rates may be used on letter-sized and flat-sized mailings. Both first-class and standard mail may qualify for presorting rates.

There are several levels of sorting. Generally, the more detailed the presort, the better the discount. Options include three-digit presorts, ZIP code presorts, and carrier-route presorts (ZIP+4).

Three-digit presorts involve sorting by the first three digits of the ZIP code. These three digits represent a Sectional Center Facility (SCF), which acts as the distribution center to Destination Delivery Units (DDU) — local post offices. One DDU usually represents one ZIP code. ZIP+4 identifies a specific range of addresses — usually one side of a city block or one floor of a building.

To qualify for a presort discount, the USPS requires mailings with a minimum of five hundred pieces for first-class and two hundred pieces for standard mailings. Mailpieces weighing more than 3.3 ounces may be subject to a surcharge. The addresses must be CASS-certified at least once per year. All pieces must be sorted and marked with the appropriate postage markings and loaded in trays or sacks.

All periodicals mail must be presorted. Presort discounts can be combined with other discounts such as automation and destination delivery discounts.

AUTOMATION

To encourage automation, the USPS provides large discounts for mailers who apply *POSTNET* barcodes on each piece. Postal Numeric Encoding Technique, or POSTNET, is a barcode system used on cards, letters, and flat mailpieces for encoding ZIP codes and, frequently, delivery-point information. The POSTNET barcode can represent a five-digit ZIP code

(32 bars), a nine-digit ZIP+4 code (52 bars), or an eleven-digit delivery point code (62 bars). This last barcode is called a *delivery-point barcode*.

These barcodes automate the mail sorting process. After the barcode has been applied, no optical character readers are needed to read the address, so the piece can bypass some of the postal sorting equipment.

Automation is different than machinable. Machinability deals with processing mail on sorting machines; automation involves machine-readable addresses — no human intervention is involved until the letter gets to the carrier. All cards and letters are processed on high-speed machines, unless their shape or size prevents it. Surcharges apply to nonmachinable mail. But even mail that is machinable may not be prepared for automated address reading.

If the address is machine-readable, a *Multi-line Optical Character Reader (MLOCR)* interprets the information on the letter-size mailpiece, and sprays the corresponding ZIP code information on the piece as a barcode. The MLOCR is the machine that reads computer-printed type and cross-references the type with a database of addresses. To qualify for automation rates, a piece must meet the following criteria:

- The address must be machine-printed, with a uniform left margin

- The address must be formatted in such a way that an MLOCR will be able to recognize the information (acceptable type style, etc.)

- The address must be complete, with directionals and designators

- Punctuation must be eliminated — all caps is preferred

- The address must include an accurate ZIP+4

- The address block must be placed in the MLOCR read area

- The piece must include a barcode-clear zone

For automation rates, the USPS requires a minimum of five hundred pieces for first-class mailings and two hundred pieces for standard mailings. The addresses must be CASS-certified within the previous 180 days of the mailing. All pieces must be 100% delivery-point barcoded, sorted, and marked with the appropriate postage markings. First-class, standard, periodicals, and BPM are all eligible for automation discounts.

DESTINATION-ENTRY DISCOUNTS

Another discount strategy saves money by using *destination-entry* discounts. In this case, rather than placing all mailpieces in the mailstream at the point of production, the mailer uses private trucks to deliver mail to various entry points in the country. The USPS rewards this activity with postal discounts.

The point of destination entry impacts rates. Twenty-one Bulk Mail Centers (BMC) — highly mechanized mail processing plants that distribute standard mail — around the country provide one level of destination entry. Several hundred SCFs provide a different level of entry. Of course, it is possible with high-density mailings to enter at specific DDUs, providing the greatest level of destination-entry discount.

Part of a magazine's postage is calculated by weight delivered to different rate zones. There are eight postal zones in the United States. Discounts can be achieved by trucking magazines to these zones before entering the mailstream. This destination entry practice is called *zone skipping* in the magazine world. Destination-entry discounts are frequently used for standard, periodicals, and BPM mailings.

COMMINGLING

A fourth discount strategy is not provided by the USPS, but rather is a way that mailing companies save their clients money. *Commingling* or *co-mailing* is the practice of taking small jobs and merging them together to achieve greater discounts. This method is used most effectively with destination-entry strategies, trucking larger shipments to various parts of the country or to meet minimums for bulk mail projects. Magazines and direct mailers utilize this strategy frequently.

By producing larger volumes, opportunities exist for smaller mailings to merge with bigger ones. Multiple magazine versions and titles are brought under one mailing. The titles do not have to be the exact same dimension or thickness. However, it needs to be presorted and, preferably, prepared for automation.

MAILPIECE DESIGN

Designing mail requires strict adherence to USPS guidelines. Failing to do so will certainly cost you money. The primary factor is to focus on designing for automation. There are four main areas of your mailpiece:

- The return address area

- The postage area

- The MLOCR read area, where the address is placed

- The barcode-clear zone

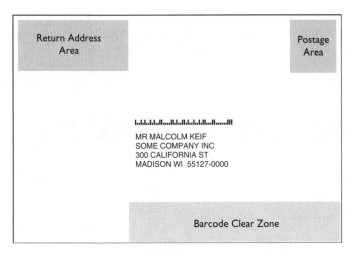

Return Address Area

Postage Area

MR MALCOLM KEIF
SOME COMPANY INC
300 CALIFORNIA ST
MADISON WI 55127-0000

Barcode Clear Zone

Figure 14-2. Insert Mailpiece Clear Zones and Free Space

Each of these elements is very specific and care is required to ensure that extraneous design elements avoid them. The MLOCR and barcode-clear zone are particularly sensitive to nonaddress components.

Additional guidelines for preparing mail include:

- Design rectangular mail

- Select a size that is within the dimensional tolerance and aspect ratio for the type of mailing you are producing (card, letter, flat, etc.)

- Use white or light-colored paper — never use reverse type for addressing

- Address parallel to the longest dimension with letters and cards

- Design a piece that seals securely

- Use a 10-12 point sans serif font (non stylized) for addressing

- Do not skew the address block more than 5°

- Use envelopes of at least 20-lb. bond or 50-lb. book stock

- For a two-panel self-mailer, use a single tab on the top or two tabs on the bottom (this requires 28-lb. bond or 70-lb. book stock)

- Tabs or seals must be white if placed in the barcode-clear zone

- Ensure that addresses display through envelope windows with a minimum or 0.25 in. clearance on all sides

ENVELOPE SIZES

There are several standard envelope sizes. Number 10 envelopes are popular for their ability to hold a standard letter-folded business letter. Number 9 envelopes are commonly used for business reply mail; these fit into a #10 envelope and still can accept an 8.5-in. wide folded business letter. Other standard envelope sizes are identified in Table F.

Booklets	
#6 1/2	6 × 9 in.
#7	6.25 × 9.625 in.
#9	8.75 × 11.5 in.
#9 1/2	9 × 12 in.
#10	9.5 × 12.625 in.
#13	10 × 13 in.
Remits	
#6 1/4	3.5 × 6 in.
#6 1/2	3.5 × 6.25 in.
#6 3/4	3.625 × 6.5 in.
#9	3.875 × 8.875 in.
#10	4.125 × 9.5 in.

Commercial	
#6 1/4	3.5 × 6 in.
#6 3/4	3.625 × 6.5 in.
#7	3.75 × 6.75 in.
#7 3/4	3.875 × 7.5 in.
#8 5/8	3.625 × 8.625 in.
#9	3.875 × 8.875 in.
#10	4.125 × 9.5 in.
#11	4.5 × 10.375 in.
#12	4.75 × 11 in.
#14	5 × 11.5 in.
Announcement	
A2	4.375 × 5.75 in.
A6	4.75 × 6.5 in.
A7	5.25 × 7.25 in.
A8	5.5 × 8.125 in.

Table F. Standard envelope sizes.

SELF-MAILERS, TABS, WAFER SEALS, AND SPOT GLUES

Self-mailers, or unenveloped letter-size mailpieces, require the open edge to be secured with an adhesive tab, or wafer seal, to prevent jamming high-speed equipment. An alternative to tabbing is to use continuous or spot glue on the open edge. Gluing is usually cheaper than tabs.

Standards for the location and number of tabs are based on the basis weight of the stock and the location of the folded edge. The important factor is that tabs do not interfere with the postage area, the FIM, or the barcode-clear zone. Consult with your mailing expert to determine the correct quantity and location of tabs.

ADDRESSING TECHNOLOGIES

Although labels are occasionally used, the majority of addressing today is done by inkjet and laser technologies.

Inkjet addressing has gained popularity as a high-speed, high-quality operation that can be performed on binding machines and even presses. Like your desktop inkjet printer, high-speed addressing equipment uses small piezo-electric heads to spray electrically charged ink in a specific pattern. Most addressing heads can image multiple lines at a time. In one quick burst, the entire address and barcode are imaged.

Magazine production is a good example. Immediately after the magazine is bound and trimmed, it passes under an inkjet imaging head. A database is consulted — the same one that was used for determining the demographic advertising to use in the magazine — and the address and barcode are imaged.

Magazines are produced in presort order. Yours is made directly after your neighbor's. This facilitates bundling the magazines in presort order for mailstream entry. If a magazine gets rejected as defective, a new one is made and hand inserted into the presort stack, or mailed separately at a higher rate.

In the direct-mail business, laser imaging may be used in addition to inkjet imaging. Roll-fed laser printers produce a large volume of the direct-mail letters and envelopes. Laser imaging generally produces cleaner type, but laser addressing is not as fast as inkjet imaging so it is not suitable for high-speed production. A common scenario is to produce letters by laser but address the envelopes with inkjet.

Inserting letters and other inserts into envelopes at high-speed is challenging. However, modern inserting equipment simplifies the process. In the case of variable, personalized letters, it is critical to match the insert to the person addressed on the envelope. Rather than rely on sequencing, it is preferred to place a small barcode on all personalized inserts. The barcodes are read, matched, and used to trigger the envelope imaging. A database is consulted and the address is sprayed on the envelope, which is sealed and placed in a tray or sack in ZIP-code order.

GLOSSARY

adhesive binding
Binding method that glues the spine of a book

aspect ratio
A mailpiece's length divided by its height. For example, a #10 envelope has an aspect ratio of 2.3 (9.5 / 4.125 = 2.3). Machinable cards and letters flats have aspect ratios from 1.3 to 2.5

basic size
Paper dimensions that are used for measuring basis weight in a given paper category

basis weight
The weight of a ream of paper cut to the basic size

bender block
Part of a stitching machine that forms the staple

bevel
Part of an embossing die that forms the transition from one plane to the next

bevel angle
Incline of the transition from one plane to the next on an embossing die

bevel in
Placement of the bevel so the incline proceeds into the image

bevel out
Placement of the bevel so the incline proceeds away from the image

bevel placement
Location of the bevel, either bevel in or bevel out

bind
To secure pages of a book

binder's board
A chipboard used in book making

blanking
Removing the useable portion of a sheet when die cutting

bleed
Extending ink to the edge of the page

bleed mark
A control mark on the press sheet that indicates where the image bleeds

blind embossing
Reshaping paper fibers to create a three-dimensional image without adding ink or foil

blow-in
Adding a reply card by blowing it into a magazine instead of binding it in

body
All pages of a book, except the cover

book block
The bound inside pages of a hardcover book before the cover is added

bottom out
Complete impression in embossing so that the die and counter die entirely touch

broaching
Removing a portion of the thickness of steel rule to increase its ability to bend at extreme angles without cracking

broadsheet
A web printed product size used in newspaper production

buckle fold
A method of folding where the paper path is abruptly stopped, buckling the paper into a set of nip rollers

buckle stop
An impediment in the folding process that buckles the paper, forcing it into the nip rollers

bulk mail center
A highly mechanized mail processing plant that distributes standard mail or package services in piece or bulk form

bunter
A heating plate used for mounting foil and embossing dies

business reply mail
A service that allows a permit holder to receive first-class mail back from customers and pay postage only for the returned pieces

caliper
The thickness of paper stock

case binding
A binding method that produces hardcover books

case making
The process of producing covers for hardcover books

casing-in
The process of applying hardcovers to book blocks

channel score
A letterpress creasing process that produces a high-quality score

chase
A frame used for locking-up a foil or embossing die

chisel edge
An embossing surface shape where all lines and shapes come to a point on the surface

closed head
When a book signature is folded along the head

coating
Sealing paper with a varnish to keep the ink on the surface; may be glossy or dull. Variations are applied on press after printing

cold foil
A process of applying a foil without a die by printing an adhesive and nipping the foil and paper while the adhesive cures

collating
The process of gathering sheets or signatures in proper sequence

comb binding
A mechanical binding method that uses a large plastic clamp to secure the pages

counter/counter die
An opposing version of an embossing die, used to ensure complete impression

cracking
Fracturing of paper and ink, revealing unsightly fiber

creep
A problem occurring on large saddle-stitched books where the inside pages stick out further than the outside pages. It is corrected by shingling

crossover
When a graphic spans the gutter, printing on two or more pages

deboss
Reshaping the paper fibers to create a three-dimensional image below the surrounding area

depth
The amount of recess or relief in an emboss

destination delivery unit
A local post office, represented by a ZIP code

destination entry discount
A postal rate discount for using private trucks to deliver mail to various postal entry points in the country

die line
A line in digital or paper form that outlines a die cut

dome
An embossing surface shape where all lines and shapes come to a dome on the surface

domestic mail manual
The USPS manual that contains the basic standards governing domestic mail services, including mail classes, rates, mail preparation, and fees

driver
The part of the wire stitcher that forces a staple through the paper

dummy
An unprinted, folded, bound replica of the final piece

dust jacket
A paper wrap put on the cover of a case-bound book for protection.

dwell
The amount of time a die remains in contact with the foil or substrate

ejection rubber
A compressible material place on steel-rule dies to force paper away after die cutting

embossing
Reshaping the paper fibers to create a three-dimensional image above the surrounding area

end sheet
The four page sheets that secure a case to a book block

facing identification mark
A series of five or six vertical bars used by automated postal equipment to identify, orient, and separate reply mail

first-class mail
A class of mail that includes all matter wholly or partly in writing or typewriting, all actual and personal correspondence, all bills and statements of account, and all matter sealed or otherwise closed against inspection

flap
A panel that is shorter than other panels

flex test
A bookbinding quality test that measures the flexibility of the spine

foil stamping
The process of transferring metal in a pattern

fold mark
A printer's mark placed on a press sheet to indicate where to fold

folio
A page number

fulfillment
The process of taking, filling, tracking, and invoicing marketing materials for franchisees or distributors

gang
Combining multiple pieces on one press sheet for increased efficiencies

GBC®
See *comb binding*

gilding
An edge treatment used for high-quality case bound books

grain direction
The alignment of cellulose fiber in one direction. Described relative to the paper's dimension — grain long or grain short

gripper edge
The edge of the paper that is fed first into a sheetfed press

guillotine cutter
A machine for making straight cuts on a stack of paper

guts
See *body*

gutter
The center margin of a book

hanger
A small flap that opposes a leaf for insertion into saddle-stitched books

high-folio
High-numbered pages

hinge cover
A cover that contains one or more hinge scores

Hinge score
A crease on adhesive-bound books that forms a hinge

imposition
The arrangement of pages on a signature. When folded, the pages are properly sequenced.

inline finishing
Sheeting, gluing, folding, die cutting, foil stamping, embossing, or some other finishing operation done on machinery in conjunction with the printing operations

inline folder/gluer
A machine for folding and gluing cartons and other items using plows to fold the stock

jog
The process of straightening the edges of a stack of paper

kiss-cut
Used with pressure-sensitive stocks; the process of die cutting without cutting the liner

kitting
Assembling various components into a single unit or package

knife fold
A folding technique that uses a dull knife to crease and force the paper into a set of nipper rollers

lap
A portion of a folded signature used by machinery to open the signature

layflat binding
An adhesive binding method that allows a book to lie flat

layout
The arrangement of a press sheet. Often diagramed or made into a template.

leaf
A two-sided sheet bound into a book. It is comprised of two pages

lip
See *lap*

lock-up
Placing and locking a die on the press or a toggle plate

loop stitch
A stitch or staple formed into a loop for insertion into ring binders

low-folio
Low-numbered pages

magnesium
A soft, light metal used in foil stamping and embossing; also called mag, as in mag dies

makeready
The preparatory process used in setting up equipment. For embossing and foil stamping, it involves careful placement of packing for even pressure

marbling
An edge treatment applied to the pages of high-quality case-bound books

marks
Control targets placed on a press sheet to aid in processing

memory (folding)
The tendency for paper to resist folding and return to flat state; most commonly occurs with thicker paper and synthetic stocks

metalizing
A method for applying aluminum to paper or plastic

multi-level die
An embossing die with two or more discrete levels

multi-line optical character reader (MLOCR)
A machine that reads an address, interprets it, and sprays a corresponding POSTNET barcode on a mailpiece

multiple-up
Placing duplicate images on a press sheet to maximize efficiency

nesting
Placing images on a press sheet to get as many pieces on as possible; the pieces are nested like a puzzle, fitting parts of one piece into the cavity of another

nick
A deliberate flaw in the steel-rule die that prevents waste from falling out on press

nipping
A case-binding stage where the backbone is flattened

notch
Uncut portions of the die board

notch binding
A strong adhesive binding method that allows increased glue penetration

packing
The material used for spot adjusting foil stamping and embossing pressure during makeready

page
A single-sided section of a book; a single leaf contains two pages

page-pull test
A bookbinding quality test that measures a book's resistance to losing pages

panel
A double-sided section of a folded piece; a letter fold is comprised of three panels

perfect binding
An adhesive-binding method that grinds, glues the spine, and three-knife trims a book

periodicals
A mailing classification used for magazines, newspapers, and other publications whose primary purpose is transmitting information to an established list of subscribers or requesters

phenolic resin
A counter-die material

plastic coil
A mechanical spiral-binding material that is more flexible than wire

plus-cover
A book with a cover made from a different stock than the interior pages. A 64-page plus cover has 64 interior pages plus a 4-page cover

pocket (binder)
A feeding station for signatures on binding machines

pocket (cover)
A pouch used for holding inserts in a folder or cover of a book; requires die cut processing

POSTNET (Postal Numeric Encoding Technique, or POSTNET)
A barcode system used on letter-size and flat-size mailpieces for encoding delivery-point and ZIP+4 information

Pragotherm®
A counter die material

preflighting
The process of checking all supplied materials upon receipt for accuracy

PUR
A glue used in adhesive binding that provides excellent adhesion in most conditions

push out
See *creep*

pyrometer
A tool for measuring face temperature of dies

quarter-fold
A web printing fold that produces signatures in 16-page increments

ram die
A die used for cutting envelopes and some labels; the stock is forced entirely through the die

ream
Five hundred sheets of a substrate

registration mark (register mark)
A mark placed on the press sheet for visually registering two or more ink colors

resist
A chemical used in the photomechanical engraving process (foil or embossing dies) that prevents the etching of the die in localized areas

ride along
An insert that is polywrapped into a magazine or catalog

ring binding
A mechanical binding method using rings that open and close for inserting paper on multiple occasions

ripple cracks
Cracks parallel to a fold when paper is bent beyond its point of elasticity; these occur when extreme forces are applied during buckle folding

rotary die cutting
A die cutting method using a curved steel-rule die or a tooled rotary die

rule
See *steel rule*

saddle
A conveying system used in saddle-stitching for inserting signatures within others prior to stitching; also called a chain

saddle-sewing
A thread sewing technique similar to saddle-stitching

saddle-stitching
A wire-stitching technique that staples from the spine to the center of a book

score
The process of creasing a stock to aid in folding without cracking

sculptured die
An embossing die that is completely analog, containing many varying depths and no discrete separation between those depths

sectional center facility
A postal facility that serves as the processing and distribution center for post offices in a designated geographic area as defined by the first three digits of a ZIP code

selective binding
A binding strategy used with magazines and catalogs where certain press signatures are included in a book based on demographic data of the reader

self-cover
A book with a cover made from the same stock as the interior pages. A 64-page self-cover has 64 total pages including the cover

sheetwise
A two-sided flat sheet imposition where the front and back are separate images

shingling
A process of compensating for creep in saddle-stitching

side-guide edge
One edge of a press sheet used for registration

side-guide mark
A mark placed on a press sheet indicating one point of registration on the printing press

side stitching
A wire-stitching method where the staple is placed from the front to the back of the book on the spine

signature
A flat press sheet containing four or more pages of a book; when folded, the pages are properly sequenced

single-level die
An embossing die where all image components are on a single plane

Smyth sewing
A popular thread sewing technique for producing case-bound books

speckling
An edge treatment for high-quality case-bound books

spine
The backbone or binding edge of a book

spiral binding
A mechanical binding method of spiraling or looping wire or plastic through a series of holes punched in a book

split bevel
An embossing technique where the bevel is placed partially into the image area and partially exterior to the image area

split double wire
A double-wire technique where the wire does not span the entire spine; two small portions bind the top and bottom of the book

spread
Two or more pages capable of having graphics span them. Reader's spreads are the two or more pages the reader sees. Printer's spreads are the two or more pages as printed in signature form

staining
An edge treatment for high-quality case-bound books

standard mail
A mailing classification used for advertising mail, catalogs, and newsletters of a non-personal nature that are not required to be mailed as first-class mail

steel rule
A die cutting, perforating, or scoring tool used for processing single sheets

step and repeat
A process for repeating an image multiple times on a press sheet to improve efficiencies

stitching
See *wire stitching*

stock
See *substrate*

stripping
A process in die cutting for removing waste

substrate
The base material for printing, embossing, or stamping

tabloid
A book or newspaper size close to 11 × 17 in.

temperature test
A test to determine the heat- or cold-resistance of adhesive bindings

thermography
A process that simulates an emboss by using a fusing powder on ink; when heated the powder melts and "puffs up"

three-knife trimming
The process of removing scrap off three sides of a book, leaving only the binding edge in tact

tipping
The process of gluing a sheet to the outside of a signature; the signature then carries the sheet through the binder

toggle
A plate that holds and heats a foil or embossing die on press

trim
The process of removing scrap from a press sheet

trim mark
A mark placed on a press sheet to indicate where to trim

v-shape edge
See *chisel edge*

wax-free ink
An ink free of Teflon®, Silicone, or other slip agents; wax-free inks are necessary for applying foil stamping and some coatings over printing

wind
The process of getting air into a stack of paper; this increases the ease with which the stack can be jogged

wire stitching
The process of forming and applying a staple

Wire-O®
See *double-wire*

work-and-back
See *sheetwise*

work-and-turn
A two-sided flat sheet imposition where the same plates are used to print both sides; the plates are two-up with front and back images. After printing, the images are cut apart and stacked in the same orientation

workflow
The steps, sequence, and techniques used for production of all or part of print production

zone skipping
A destination-entry strategy used with periodicals and bound printed matter to discount postage by traveling to different USPS rate zones before entering the mailstream

INDEX

S

saddle-stitching   5, 41, 57-70, 71, 73, 74-75, 82, 83, 84, 94, 95
scoring   6, 13, 31-33, 43, 55-56, 60, 62, 73
sculptured dies   119-120, 127
Sectional Center Facility (SCF)   150, 152
selective binding   61
self-mailers   154
service requests   147
shingling   69
shipping   4, 6, 13, 22, 85, 134, 136-139
shrink-wrapping   13, 135
side glue   75
side-stitching   60, 91
signatures   9, 11, 20-21, 23, 41, 43, 45, 51, 54, 55, 60, 61, 62, 63, 64, 65, 66, 67, 68, 69, 70, 73, 74, 75, 76, 77, 78, 79, 80, 81, 82, 83, 87, 91, 93, 94, 95, 99
single-level dies   117-118, 125-126
skid packing   136-137
slip sheets   99, 136
spine glue   75
spiral coil binding   58, 84-88
spot glues   154
stamping dies   103-105
standard mail   144-145
stapling   59
steel-rule die   32-35
stitching   5, 13, 20, 41, 71, 73-75, 82-84, 87, 91, 94-95
stitching heads   62-63

stripping   35-37
substrate   7, 14, 18, 23, 33, 35-36, 39-40, 43, 46, 55-56, 57, 71, 72, 75, 76, 82-84, 97, 98, 99, 101-103, 106, 108, 111-112, 113-117, 123, 126, 127-128. See also *paper*
super calendared (SC) papers   17

T

tabs   154
temperature tests   79
thermography   114-115
thread sewing   93-95
three-knife trimming   63
tipping   21, 66, 95
tooled rotary dies   36-37
transit marking   99, 133-135
trapping   13
trimming   23-28, 77, 96

U

U.S. Postal Service (USPS)   6, 8, 10, 41, 66, 139-141, 147-152

V

varnishes   5, 40, 56, 134
Velo binding   58, 90

W

wafer seals   154
warehousing   4, 7
wire stitching   20, 57, 59, 62, 71, 87
Wire-O   5, 58, 83, 84, 86.
     See also *double-wire*
workflow   73-80, 115-124

ABOUT THE AUTHOR

Malcolm G. Keif is a professor in the Graphic Communication Department at Cal Poly State University, San Luis Obispo. A Cal Poly alum, he completed his Ph.D. with an emphasis in Technology Teaching from the University of Missouri in 1995.

He has worked for both high-quality heat-set web and sheetfed printing companies and provides on-sight training and consulting for various companies. His teaching responsibilities have included courses in binding, finishing, and distribution systems; web offset, flexographic and gravure printing technologies; and quality management. Throughout his career, he has instructed coursework in various aspects of color reproduction and postpress finishing.

ABOUT NAPL

NAPL is dedicated to helping the graphic arts community succeed within today's highly competitive communications environment. We help our members by offering educational, consulting, and member services, for both companies and individuals.

LEARN MORE ABOUT NAPL

www.napl.org

(Order online) Bookstore
http://store.napl.org

Membership Information
www.napl.org/napl/what_is_napl.htm

Contact Us
Phone: 800-642-6275, option #3
Fax: 201-634-0328
Email: Products@napl.org

75 West Century Road
Paramus, NJ 07652

ALSO AVAILABLE

NAPL Proprietary Books

Product Code	Title
NP326	Benchmarking the Bindery
NP325	Benchmarking The Prepress Workflow
NP327	Benchmarking The Web Pressroom
NP350	Bulding a Digital Services Portfolio
NP354	Cross-Media Cookbook: A Strategy Primer
NP321	Compensating Your Customer Service Representatives
NP322	Compensating Your Print Sales Managers
NP303	Compensating Your Sales Personnel
NP331	Customer-Centered Production
NP348	Customer Creation
NP346	Designer's Prepress Companion
NP353	Designer's Printing Companion
NP312	Exceeding Expectations
NP338	Getting & Keeping The Staff You Deserve
NP316	Hands-On Marketing For the Printer
NP340	How Fulfillment Services Drive Print Volume
NP337	How To Succeed In a Family-Run Printing Business
NP323	How To Write Profit-Building Sales Letters
NP347	The Human Resources Guide For Graphic Arts Managers
NP336	Managing & Selling Digital Prepress
NP345	The NAPL 2002-2003 State of The Industry Report
NP319	NAPL Business Writing Handbook
NP328	Plan To Profit
NP301	The Pricing Game
NP360	A Printer's Guide to Content Management Services
NP329	The Printer's Guide to Waste Reduction
NP352	Print Production Workflow
NP339	Sales Force Automation & Customer Relationship Management
NP320	Strategic Sales Management
NP341	Successfully Selling The New Breed Of Print Buyers
NP342	SuperCharge Your Print Sales
NP330	Take The Risk Out of Hiring Print Salespeople
NP357	Understanding Information Technology for Print Management
NP344	Unleashing Your Print Sales/Business Negotiating Skills
NP349	The Winning Sales Call

ALSO AVAILABLE

NAPL Blue Books

Product Code	Title
NB110	Hourly Cost Studies for Bindery, Finishing & Mailing Operations
NB111	Hourly Cost Studies for Digital Prepress Operations
NB107	Hourly Cost Studies for Print Operations Up to 20 Employees
NB109	Hourly Cost Studies for Sheetfed Press Operations
NB104	Hourly Cost Studies for Web Press Operations

NAPL Pocket University Series

Product Code	Title	Product Code	Title
NR101	Acrobat PDF	NR117	Mac OS
NR102	Basic Color	NR118	Paper
NR103	Color Management	NR119	Photoshop
NR104	CTP	NR120	PostScript
NR105	Digital Asset Management	NR121	Preflighting
NR106	Digital Photography	NR122	Presses and Printing
NR107	Digital Printing	NR123	Proofing
NR108	Drawing Programs	NR124	Raster Files
NR109	E-business	NR125	Recorded Media
NR110	File Formats	NR126	RIPs
NR111	Fonts and Font Management	NR127	Scanning
NR112	Halftones	NR128	Trapping
NR113	HTML	NR129	Variable Data Printing
NR114	Image Basics	NR130	Vector & EPS
NR115	Imposition and Bindery	NR131	Wide Format Printing
NR116	Layout Programs	NR132	Windows
		NR133	Workflow
		NR134	XML

ALSO AVAILABLE

Multimedia and Software

CS InterAct Blue Book Cost Studies on CD-ROM
ND110	CS InterAct - BD Bindery & Finishing Edition
ND111	CS InterAct - PR Digital Prepress Edition
ND109	CS InterAct - SF Sheetfed Edition
ND104	CS InterAct - WB Web Press Edition

NAPL Audio Cassettes
NA804	Long Run Growth Leaders
NA805	Managing Your Sales Staff (Terry A. Nagi)
NA806	Hiring & Training Your Sales Staff (Terry A. Nagi)
NA807	Fulfillment Warehouse (Clint Bolte)
NA808	Training Your Sales Staff (Peter Ebner)
NA809	Managing Your Sales Staff (Peter Ebner)
NA810	Hiring Your Sales Staff (Peter Ebner)

NAPL CDs
ND800	Long Run Growth Leaders
ND801	Managing Your Sales Staff
ND802	Hiring & Training Your Sales Staff
ND803	Fulfillment Warehouse
ND804	Training Your Sales Staff
ND805	Managing Your Sales Staff
ND806	Hiring Your Sales Staff
ND811	The Economy & Its Effect On the Printing Industry
ND812	Sales Force Automation & Customer Relationship Management
ND813	Is E-Business The Future of Print?
ND814	Executive Compensation & Benefits
ND815	Building The Value of Your Business
ND816	The Printing Industry & The Economy Since September 11th
ND817	Software Violations: Are You At Risk?

NEW FROM NAPL

PRINT PRODUCTION WORKFLOW: A PRACTICAL GUIDE

NAPL Member Price: $29.95
Non-Member Price: $34.95

Product Code: NP352

Today's successful graphic arts companies need a seamlessly integrated, efficient, and productive workflow. Yet, given the dizzying rate at which new technologies are emerging and the wide range of available options, developing a world-class workflow can be a daunting task. In *Print Production Workflow: A Practical Guide* by Chuck Gehman, you will discover a wealth of valuable information for printers, service bureaus, ad agencies, and publishing houses on the benefits and limitations of specific workflow solutions, including those based on conventional, digital, Internet-enabled digital, and hybrid systems. Also included is a comprehensive digest of the available systems and solutions referenced in the book.

A PRINTER'S GUIDE TO CONTENT MANAGEMENT SERVICES

NAPL Member Price: $29.95
Non-Member Price: $34.95

Product Code: NP360

As companies become increasingly aware of the value of their investment in corporate content and the intellectual capital it represents, they are eager to gain full profit potential by leveraging this significant investment to lower costs, improve productivity, and harness their creative assets faster than their competition. *A Printer's Guide to Content Management Services: Profiting from Content in the Digital Age* by Cary Sherburne demystifies the field of content management services by citing real-world examples drawn from a variety of successful service providers who have augmented their businesses by adding content management services to their portfolio of offerings.

DESIGNER'S PRINTING COMPANION

NAPL Member Price: $24.95
Non-Member List Price: $29.95

Product Code: NP353

Written to be easily understood and absorbed by newcomers as well as experienced graphic design professionals, *Designer's Printing Companion* offers an introduction and clear explanation of the computer-to-plate and printing processes, from lithography, flexography and gravure, to screen printing, letterpress, and digital printing technology. In plain language and an easy-to-follow format, *Designer's Printing Companion* distills this complex information to the important points graphic designers, students, and industry newcomers need to know. A great customer giveaway!

NEW FROM NAPL

BUILDING A DIGITAL SERVICES PORTFOLIO

NAPL Member Price: $29.95   *Product Code: NP350*
Non-Member List Price: $34.95

Building A Digital Services Portfolio presents a clear and compelling argument for
augmenting conventional printing services with a full spectrum of digital services
designed to increase customer loyalty and capture a greater share of customer
spend. Loaded with advice, guidance, and links to easily available resources,
Building a Digital Services Portfolio will help you understand the importance of
unmet customer needs and implement an affordable strategy for meeting them.

DESIGNER'S PREPRESS COMPANION

NAPL Member Price: $24.95   *Product Code: NP346*
Non-Member List Price: $29.95

A no-nonsense, step-by-step desk reference guide for graphic artist professionals,
design students, and/or anyone who wants to gain a better understanding of
prepress and digital design. In clear language and an easy-to-follow format,
Designer's Prepress Companion outlines every phase of the printing process, both
traditional and digital. An outstanding customer giveaway!

ALSO AVAILABLE IN SPANISH...
GUÍA DE PREIMPRESIÓN DEL DISEÑADOR   *NP346S*

Como una invaluable ayuda de enseñanza y un manual con instrucciones detalladas
la Guia de preimpresión del diseñador es la primera opción como guía de referencia
del artista gráfico.

PRINTSHOP 101 (SOFTWARE)

NAPL Member Price: $199.95   *Product Code: XD112*
Non-Member List Price: $299.95

This print shop interactive basic training on CD-ROM includes more than 1,000
color screen pages filled with easy-to-understand language, diagrams, photographs,
drawings and animation. PrintShop 101 will help you improve customer
satisfaction with a well-trained staff who know how to deal with problems and
reduce time and materials waste to increase profit on every job. This self-paced tool
can be used to train one employee or an entire staff at one affordable price. (PC
compatible only.)

National Association for Printing Leadership   800-642-6275 • www.napl.org